# BETWEEN TWO MOONS

# BETWEEN TWO MOONS

## A Technicolor Travelogue

by Raymond Mungo

Beacon Press  Boston

DESIGN & GRAPHICS BY
RICHARD C. BARTLETT

Copyright © 1972 by Raymond Mungo,

Library of Congress catalog card number: 70–179153

International Standard Book Number:
   0–8070–6402–5 (hardcover)
   0–8070–6405–X (paperback)

Beacon Press books are published under the auspices
of the Unitarian Universalist Assocation

Published simultaneously in Canada
by Saunders of Toronto, Ltd.

Printed in the United States of America

of by and for Love

When in the chronicle of wasted time
I see descriptions of the fairest wights,
And beauty making beautiful old rhyme,
In praise of ladies dead, and lovely knights;
Then in the blazon of sweet beauty's best,
Of hand, of foot, of lip, of eye, of brow,
I see their antique pen would have express'd
Even such a beauty as you master now.
So all their praises are but prophecies
Of this our time, all you prefiguring;
And, for they look'd but with divining eyes,
They had not skill enough your worth to sing;
    For we, which now behold these present days,
    Have eyes to wonder, but lack tongues to praise.

Wm. Shakespeare

## THE CAST

♓ ABRAHAM, a young man, junkie/saint and world savior, Zero Degree Pisces with moon in Scorpio. It all just happens to him.

♏ *RUTH, a young woman, poetess/earth-mother, and insatiably hungry. Scorpio in her sun and five planets, moon in Cancer. She makes it all happen.*

♋ THE FOX, the mastermind good Cancer genie, hopelessly alone. Dead.

♉ **NEGRO-LADY driving a 1956 Buick. She tended Jacob's horses.**

♏ MRS. LAWRENCE, 67 years in this body, a surrogate Scorpio mother.

♌ YALE, a clean-cropped young businessman and ambassador.

♏ *FERGUSON, a local dairy farmer and free rapacious spirit. He hits the bottle.*

♌ **SILENT**, *looks like Harpo Marx, keeps dogs and secrets. He's the real Leo poet among us.*

♓ MAD JOHN, another Pisces, noncommercial rock 'n'roll star. Lean and lately removed from Australia, a man of moods.

↦ JACOB, con-man farmer pilgrim and bum. He's the original Sagittarian force, and nothing will stop him now.

♌ WONDERBOY, who could make the winter green at a tender age, and stole away with Moonbeam to give her a boychild.

♏ *MOONBEAM, mother lover sister daughter princess and star.*

♌ **UNCLE LOUIE, gigantic Cuban teacher father and conga-drum midnight wail.**

♌ *MARIE, a black-magic woman from Paris, daughter of homicidal madness, and desperate searcher for perfect love.*

≈ TOM & RICHARD, a pair of missionaries of Mandrake Plains and the Aquarian Age.

♍ CRANE, a tortured Virgo intellectual poet and political radical fresh from New York.

♏ **MOONBEAM'S BABY. Son of Wonderboy, and heir to the Fox, Jacob, and Ruth.**

♏ **MAMOUSHKA, famed marijuana-sniffing white Samoyed dog. Still another Scorpio lady, and mother to millions.**

♏ **GREGORY, tyrant guru agent hypnotist and leader of Mandrake Plains. He rules.**

♎ *OLD MAN, fisherman, the principle of Libra, the scales, justice.*

♌ **JUNIOR, who witnessed the end.**

♐ *BIG MARTY, benign Sagittarian strongman who held it all together after the end.*

♓ THE NARRATOR, who creates Paradise only to lose it again. Me.

SCENE ONE

NARRATOR'S VOICE: I can't remember when it was that I
first began making the movie. For a long time it was just
happening to me, then one morning I was *making* it
happen. I didn't know, then, what I was getting into. I
never bargained for *this* movie.

(IMAGE: It is dawn in the whole city, and a rouge-
red slither rising reflected in the ocean waters,
seen from above the highest buildings and on top
of a cloud of grey smoke and smog which hangs sus-
pended over part of the tableau.

(Nothing is moving but the sharpest ears will hear
this sunrise scene trembling: a constant whine,
low in volume but high in pitch, under all.

(The Narrator's voice is calm but almost
ethereal, peaceful but not cool. Clearly, he re-
spects the intensity of the story he's about to
tell: maybe, we can tell, he's even afraid.)

NARRATOR'S VOICE: I *thought* I was making a movie about
blood and thunder and guts, all the great confrontations
of our age. There'd be battle and rape, victory and defeat,
and maybe even an ironic twist at the end: winning is

really *losing,* etcetera. And I thought I had something to say. In fact, I thought and thought and thought and you know it didn't get me *anywhere.* I mean my movie began in my mind and ended up in my heart.

Also I figured out that everybody had already *seen* that old movie, the great epic of the power of ideas in conflict. And in *this* scene, the hero blows up a computer company, and the feds are after him. O, it's all an attempt to convince you of something, mostly that something's *wrong* out there when there's nothing wrong out there, never has been, but only in our lousy minds.

(The sun is rising. The trembling grows louder.)

So that was the end of my movie, or so I thought then. It was just more of the same old shit, I was bored, it was a rerun at a crummy drive-in theater, the second feature was about wife-swapping in that coy way where the guy never really gets his friend's wife in bed, except the time he falls through the upstairs bathroom floor and into her astonished arms. To hell with it, anyone who needs to go out of his own backyard to witness people's pathetic hangups and cold violence oughta *stay home.*

Great changes came then, the movie started in earnest and I didn't know where it would end or how long it'd last or what would happen next. And yeah of course I had no reason not to hope for a happy ending.

The changes made it so much better, that's what it's all about, and it was suddenly so *real*—not cardboard people fighting for crazy imaginary ideals but flesh and blood flowing through cornfields—and all the people had color in their cheeks and their food was hot and steaming on wooden tables and their animals followed them about—not kid stuff anymore, but life or death my movie became. It took my breath away, and left me silent for a long time. I guess I can't tell you even now, I guess you know this movie as well as *I* do.

My mind led me up against stone walls of words and ideas and opinions—abstractions, y'know, and *notions* about life substituted for the genuine item. My heart led me up primrose thorny paths, you-n-me sagas, over mountain ranges, down into the valley of death. It was thrilling.

I hated my own incapacity to take the *initiative* of love; love was something that would *happen* to me and I couldn't or didn't make it happen. My friends wondered what the touch of me would be like.

So it came to me finally, a choice between paths: movement or holding still, city or country, the Work or the Life, mind or heart, male or female, romantic or

classical. What'll it be, my genie said to me, Truth or Power? I opted always, or strove to, to go higher. Higher. To go as high as I could before I fell.

For a while there, it looked to be a sad movie. (Always make me cry.) The way of the heart is as troublesome, in its fashion, as the life of the mind.

But hell. This was all a long time ago.

*     *     *

(The sun is rising, it is risen: red globe. The noise grows.)

It changed my mind to heart, and I smiled. It moved from philosophy to anecdote. This movie became just what happens. That, I finally realized, is more than enough.

(Traffic is moving now, and the increasing buzz level of the city is gently and gradually drowned by who else but The Incredible String Band singing "Maya." The tempo of their song changes repeat-edly, from minstrel simplicity and beauty to hard, pullulating rhythms. The camera takes in the streets more carefully, catching Abraham fall-ing off a first-floor porch into a garbage-crammed alleyway, laughing. The door between porch and interior of this grey-shingled slum

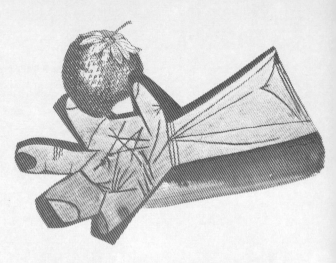

tenement building opens, and a blue pillow flies
out, striking him square on the head. Behind the
curtained window, a laughing black-eyed girl with
long black hair to her generous breasts: Ruth.

(Abe has long brown hair, flopping and embracing
his shoulder blades, he's 21 years old, he's wearing a standard white T-shirt and faded jeans with
a rip in the right knee.

(Camera follows him through dingy 49-cent-break-
fast greasy spoon coffee and cigarette, reading
newspaper, smoking cigarettes, run for city bus,
entering office with floor strewn with colorful
literature and plywood desks set up on City Water
Department sawhorses, a demonstration, a lec-
ture, a phone conversation, an argument in the
street, a hostile glare between Abraham and a second long-haired fellow, this one with kinky black
curls like Harpo Marx and wearing long amber
Moroccan chillaba, barefoot, scratching his
crotch through the robe: it's The Fox.

(Camera follows these and other typical intown
scenes, begging for quarters at the airport, a
bloody head meeting a policeman's club, dissen-

sion, confusion, finally chaos. Meanwhile The Incredible String Band is all we can hear and the
credits are superimposed for us to read.)


## MAYA

### Words by Robin Williamson


The dust of the rivers does murmur and weep
Hard and sharp laughter that cuts to the bone
Ah, but every face within your face does show
Going gladly now to give himself his own.

And twelve yellow willows shall follow the
    shallows
Small waves and thunder be my pillow
Upon the gleaming water two swans that swim
And every place shall be my native home.

The east gate like a fortress dissolve it away
The west gate like a prison O come break it down
Island I remember living here
Wandering beneath the empty skies.

In time her hair grew long and swept the ground
And seven blackbirds carried it out behind
It bore the holy imprint of her mind
As green-foot slow she moved among the seasons.

The great man, the great man
Historians his memory
Artists his senses
Thinkers his brain
Labourers his growth
Explorers his limbs
And soldiers his death each second
And mystics his rebirth each second
businessmen his nervous system
no-hustle men his stomach
astrologers his balance
lovers his loins
His skin it is all patchy
but soon will reach one glowing hue.
God is his soul
infinity his goal
the mystery his source and civilization:
He leaves behind
opinions on his fingernails.

Maya! Maya!
All this world is but a play:
Be thou the joyful player!

Maya! Maya!

All this world is but a play:
Be thou the joyful player!

The wanderer no sense does make
his eyes being tied in the true love's knot
The trees perceive his soul.
Do not detain him long.

Dear little animal dark-eyed and small
caring for your fur with pointed paws
This hawk of truth is swift and flies with a
  still cry
A small sweetmeat to the eyes of night.

O dandelion be thou thine
Reflecting the sun in sexual glory
in ever-changing tongues
The ever-changing story.

The book
man
bird
woman
serpent
sea
sun
Blessed O blessed are they of the air
your eyes are the eyes
of the glad land
Ye twelve that will enter the seasons.

The great ship, the ship of the world
Long time sailing
Mariners, mariners: gather your skills.

The great ship, the ship of the world,
Long time sailing
Mariners, mariners: gather your skills.

Jesus and Hitler and Richard the Lionheart
Three kings and Moses and Queen Cleopatra
The cobbler, the maiden,
The mender and the maker,
The sickener and the twitcher
and the glad undertaker
the shepherd of willows
the harper and the archer:
All sat down in one boat together:
Troubled voyage in calm weather.

   Maya! Maya!
   All this world is but a play:
   Be thou the joyful player!

   Maya! Maya!
   All this world is but a play:
   Be thou the joyful player!

      *       *      *

      End of Scene One

SCENE TWO

(SOUND: Car-door slam is loud, the sharp click of
the doorlock is the final note of the song "Maya":
this click of the door also lets us know that the
overture is complete. We no longer hear music but
now the low staccato rumble of a car radio tuned to
a twenty-four-hour news station comes through the
sound.

(IMAGE: Car-door slamming, a 1956 Buick, black
with two large gaping rusted-out holes in its
side, the door of this vehicle fills the entire
screen. Shot is from behind the car and facing
forward and as soon as the door slams the car takes
off, clearly a hitchhiker has just gotten in. We
watch the old Buick drive off, we are on a highway,
three lanes of cars whizzing by, it is Connect-
icut, northbound.

(IMAGE: The front seat of the Buick, a very large
Negro-lady at the wheel. Abraham sits on the pas-
senger-side of the front seat, between him and the
ageless (all-ages), sexless (all-sexes) driver
is his dark green army rucksack. On the dashboard

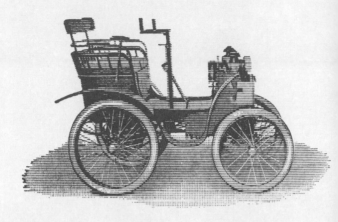

of the car, directly in front of Abraham, the camera has now become his eyes and we are seeing through them, is a cheap plastic religious artifact, a sign: TRUST IN THE LORD; in fact, the front of the car we are riding in is carefully decked with such icons: a cross of two thin twigs bound with white twine and nestled in between two pine cones, and a faded newspaper photograph of the late Otis Redding Scotch-taped on the dash, etc., etc. A pack of Kool Filter-King cigarettes is carefully nestled in behind the TRUST IN THE LORD sign.)

**NEGRO-LADY: Where you headed?**

ABRAHAM: North.

(IMAGE: A flaming cloth covers her wizened head, the color of the kerchief offset by the craggy darkness of her face, she is fifty years old, sixty, perhaps seventy? A few white hairs sparkle on her chin, not a beard but a nanny-goat's tuft. She turns to face her passenger, the kid-hitchhiker, and now we get a full shot of her face, she grins and a gold-capped tooth peeks out of her mouth like the sun.)

**NEGRO-LADY: You in college?**

ABRAHAM: No, I've been out of school for about a year, been livin' in the city and working for the Movement. But I just gotta get out for a while, get some air.

**NEGRO-LADY: You goin' far, ain't you? (Her eyes let us know that she knows where Abraham is going, even though he may not: the Negro-lady now turned gypsy, her eye takes us all the way back—through the smoke of a Kool cigarette—back to the crystal-ball voodoo of the West Indies.)**

ABRAHAM: I'm going to meet some friends, up in the mountains, they've got some land there. And planting season is just about starting now, I guess.

**NEGRO-LADY: My people had a place in Carolina, weren't much more'n two acres, then there was the house, the barn a little ways away, that's where we kept Jacob's horses . . . (She stamps out the cigarette and now inserts a toothpick into one corner of the soft, thick curling flesh of her mouth. Lips dark-red and juicy, the toothpick a sliver of white wood.)**

**Now Jacob was a fine figure of a man, and to see him swagger around the barn with the stallion you'd say he was the king, you know, the leader. He'd like the stallion hisself, you know, wild and strong like that but living in a nice barn after all. O, he weren't no fool.**

He carried the load of us, me and my grandpappy and the kids, he made it nice for us to live on that old two acres and we never wanted for nothin'. Yes we was happy kids. Jacob carried us but he get tired in the end and we had to carry *him* sometimes y'see? But we always made it, h'yes.

O and sometimes the moon'd be out and we'd sing songs you know by Jake's banjo.

ABRAHAM: This was a while ago?

NEGRO-LADY: Don't seem but like yesterday.

ABRAHAM: He was your brother?

NEGRO-LADY: Who?

ABRAHAM: Jacob.

NEGRO-LADY: O he was a man, I was a woman, course it was *in my youth*, y'see.

ABRAHAM: (Embarrassed, he turns his eyes to the floor) O.

(Both stare ahead at the road. The news-radio is now faintly audible through the static and car-on-road sounds: "And in Memphis tonight, wanted killer Willie Fred Mason was surrounded and shot by deputies of the state police barracks following a frantic chase down downtown streets," etc.)

**NEGRO-LADY: You got a girl waiting for you?**

ABRAHAM: Yes . . . no . . . Well it's not like that actually. Well it's hard to explain.

**NEGRO-LADY: Well never mind explainin' honey, explainin' never helped much anyway.**

ABRAHAM: No I don't mind telling you . . . I just wonder if you could understand, cause I don't really understand it myself. You see, I'm not sure whether I'm male or female, that is, I think I'm both, and it bothers me cause I'm not used to it. So I don't know whether it's a *girl* I've got waiting for me, or another creature of all sexes and ages. Does that make sense to you?

**NEGRO-LADY: H'yes, h'yes, that's all a little over my head honey but I reckon you gonna figure it all out OK eventually.**

ABRAHAM: (Laughing) I hope so. I feel very silly being bothered by it. I hope so.

**NEGRO-LADY: You got to trust in the Lord. He make everything good and right, don't He? He ain't made no mistakes, has He?**

ABRAHAM: (Laughing again) No mistakes!

**NEGRO-LADY: Well ain't it true? Ain't it?**

ABRAHAM: Yes you're right. It's perfect. (Laughing.) It's perfect.

(Abraham laughs freely, with a glint in his full open eyes. He is beginning to let go. He is learning to surrender. The trip is beginning. He is getting ready for his fall.)

NEGRO-LADY: Well, *Amen.*

(IMAGE: The highway flowing by as seen through the windshield of the old Buick, a frame whose border is formed by the various religious curios. We are clearly leaving the vibrational reach of the city, civilization's encrusted heart. We are in search of the transplant, the psychic transplant. Road signs begin to thin out; and now there are less factories, industrial parks on the side of the highway. The Negro-Lady's voice is heard, but off camera; the sun is setting, it is getting dimmer, the light, and now her voice takes on an almost Aunt Jemima quality.)

NEGRO LADY: (Off-camera) My momma grew string-beans and corn, an' me'n my sisters we worked them weeds. H'yes, h'yes, we had some chickens and an old devil-rooster we called Brutus. He sure was somethin' else, mean? my word was he *bad.* But you

know, I was just a girl then. Farmin', it's mostly for the children, I
reckons.

(SOUND: The all-news radio station has dissolved
almost unnoticed into music, just as the scenery
has become more rural, the road is opening up;
night has overtaken day, the car headlights now
reflect the road. Still through the radio we hear
some nondescript commercialized be-bop music.)

NEGRO-LADY: (Still off-camera) We left Carolina when Lucy married
and her man wantin' to go north. That's where they all goin', ain't
it? Say, you want some coffee? Reach f' that Thermos back
there, it's in the basket there in the back seat.

ABRAHAM: Far out! I could really dig some coffee right about
now.

(IMAGE: Abraham turns round to go through the
wicker basket, he fishes out the large Thermos, it
is worn, the paint on the outside is chipped;
Abraham pours a steaming cupful into the Thermos
top. The scene is shot through the backseat, we
see the backs of their heads and the front windshield, the highway.)

NEGRO-LADY: (No longer off-camera; we now get a shot of the driver

and her passenger as seen from outside the windshield looking
in, the old woman is still talking, she is hypnotized by the road.
Abraham sips the coffee and watches her seriously as she
continues talking.) Daddy Jacob he tol' us we wuz bein' foolish
goin' north, he said everything a body needed was right there in
that two acres, but we wuz young and we cussed him and tol'
him he an old fool. We sure thought we had somethin' on him,
h'yes, h'yes, but peekin' at it from this side it looks to me the
old fox sure knew what he was talkin'. City didn't have no
more'n them cement (pronounced cee-ment) streets, oh they had
the dollah, to be sure.

(IMAGE: Camera comes in close on her face through
the windshield, it is dark everywhere but the
dashboard light hits her face and bounces back at
us in the form of twinkling lights. It is late at
night, we follow the car on the highway, perhaps
it begins to rain.

(SOUND: We hear Neil Young singing "The Old
Laughing Lady," approximately three or four minutes long, and by the end of the song, the sun has
risen once again, another day. The car pulls to a
halt on a lonely rock-and-dirt country road.
Abraham gets out, pulls his pack out and closes

the door. He leans into the window, camera inside
the car.)

ABRAHAM: I sure wanta thank you for bringing me all this
way, ma'm. And thanks for the sign.

**NEGRO-LADY: No problem honey, just trust in the lord and watch out
fo' Jacob's Horses, h'yes-h'yes (and we see the car pull away,
turn around, and head back toward where presumably the main
road lies).**

\*       \*       \*

End of Scene Two

SCENE THREE

(It is an Eastcoast movie, certainly, but the city
from whence Abraham comes, and the magic village
his destination are out of time and space. They
are never identified: there is even some am-
biguity about which country we are in. They are so
much the same. Certain recent conveniences give
it away as a modern story, but somehow all evidence of automation must melt smoothly into the
material circumstances, while our attention is
focused on the natural things happening: people,
animals, and land. The village could be anywhere
where the high hills around are green, red, orange, yellow, brown, and white depending on one of
four distinct seasons, and trees of all sorts grow
in great profusion; the roads are all horse-
paths, and the land rocky but unspoiled. It's a
New England movie, I guess.

(Abraham is on one such trail, which opens up by an
old fieldstone fence on a 50-mile view of the
green mountains ahead, and beyond them white-cap-
ped peaks higher still. In his immediate view are
numbers of meadows sweetly green for July, tops of

little houses and barns, much forest. He is wearing the same torn jeans, a white T-shirt and an Army surplus knapsack on his back, now with a floppy old felt hat, grey, dark eyeglasses, and old clodhopper boots that lace up the front.

(It is summer. He is on a voyage, journey, ascension. He's a mountain-climber, forest-tramper, stream-jumper. Though his body is not what we call athletic in a superb way, it is limber, suntanned and vibrant. He is beautiful, a crazy dark-spectacled junkie/saint child alone in fantastic natural surroundings. He is clearly full of wonderment.

(There is no music but birds and wind, and no words. Abraham does not talk to himself, but occasionally bursts into song. Sometimes he abandons his song in mid-verse, as, say, some black cow with a white nose moos at him. He sings fragments of "Danny Boy," "Amazing Grace," and the old spiritual, "You Got to Walk That Lonesome Valley [By Yourself]."

(He stops under a maple tree, opens his pack, removes a blue cloth pouch, methodically rolls a joint, smokes it, laughs, shakes his head, he

can't believe it. He then takes off the dark
glasses and pushes on, staggering slightly,
laughing, says only "O wow."

(He eats Underwood Deviled Ham spread on slices of
bread from the store: white bread.

(Day is turning gradually to night. As the sun
moves down into its evening bed crimson, he finds
himself now on the opposite side of a river running through a cleared area with a spacious
western horizon. The river is at once too wide and
deep to walk across, and too narrow to require a
boat or bridge. The water reflects the spectac-
ular sunset and ripples over a hidden boulder. It
looks cold.

(He knows what he has to do. He strips quickly,
stuffing his gear into the pack, and eases into
the water, paddling with one arm and holding the
pack aloft with the other. Not quite enough
strength there, and the pack slowly sinks a moment
before he reaches the other shore. Now he too is
wet and sparkling red with the sun. He wraps his
arms around his beaded chest, shivering.

(Abe's got a white strip across his body where his
bathing trunks interfered with the sun.

(Night is here, the stars are clear and twinkling. He gets up a rather bad fire, poking it constantly, hanging up wet clothes on the limbs of a tree over the fire, finally climbing into a red sleeping bag and turning his eyes upward. He sighs, smiles and falls asleep.

(Day returns, maybe the next day or 20 days later: anyway, a new place: higher and more barren. A scramble from a deep fresh-water gorge up a near-vertical cliff, breathless and close to disaster.

(A dark wood, mostly pine and spruce. Confusion and frustration: anxiety at being possibly lost. Stops to look around, carefully searching for a sign. An old gate, wrought-iron, hanging hinged on slate uprights attracts him.

(The gate leads into a cemetery now beginning to become overgrown with saplings, small trees, high grass, ferns. All the stones are very old, thin slabs of marble or slate with barely legible words. Abraham stoops to rub one stone with a sleeve. It reads:

Rebecca Chapman

1762-1781

Two weeks I bore affliction sore
Physicians' skill was vain.
But in the end death came as friend
to ease me of my pain.
Death is a debt, from all 'tis due
Which I have paid and so must you.

The grave near it is open, a deep hole in the
earth, but clearly not fresh. Its headstone lies
on the ground, broken into two pieces.

(A light appears in the forest, the ordeal is
nearly over. It grows larger as Abraham approaches it; he's sure it's open land and rushes
to it. He bursts from the forest facing camera
exultant and glowing, smiling, his eyes are ex-
ploding. Camera turns from his full face to his
prospect: It is a huge open field and steep hill,
he is at the top of it. The earth is green everywhere, trees are full, it is an orchard, and vis-
ible below, a cluster of three tiny houses with,
variously, blue, red, and white rooves, and a
bright red barn. A brown dirt road divides the
village, or perhaps holds it together.

(A wind comes up and shakes the trees like paper banners at a parade. They dip and tremble and howl. Abraham begins running and falling down the hill, and disappears or disintegrates into the unspoiled landscape.

(It is a dream, this trial, this journey. Yet it is over-real, not vague and soft, but rich and distinct, overwhelming sensation. Dreamily, though, he's gone.

(The scene is still the magic village from afar in July.)

RUTH'S VOICE: *Abraham! It's time to* wake up!

\*     \*     \*

End of Scene Three

SCENE FOUR

(The narrator is back on sound while the camera
sees Abraham's eyes, casually shut, burst open.
His eyes are brown. Beside him in the bed is Ruth,
who's eagerly talking to him.

(The narrator's voice suggests he is a very old
and experienced Vermont woodsman and local coot,
and these are his reminisces.)

NARRATOR'S VOICE: When I first arrived there, I was
confused and a little elated. It looked like a new planet to
me, and it *was*—to me. Others had been there millions of
years before and we couldn't always tell how old our
neighbors were. Sometimes they were like babies, crying
and cooing—other times they were ancient sages of this
cold mountain, our Fountain of Youth.

The place had a name, or many names actually. Trouble
was it was always changing. In the summer I thought it
was maybe in South America, lost on the Andes of Peru or
something; by winter it was some barren merciless tundra
in the gone Ukraine. Old Ed, our closest neighbor in the
village, often called it Earth, but the Spirit Lake people
called it the Whole World. As well it was. There was no

place to go from there, and no way out, until your time came. The Fox called it the Village and secretly always wanted to be Village Clerk. And lots of people called it Noplace, or Neverland, and never believed their own lives thereafter—it was all some fantasy. And why not? no deeds or recorded evidence suggested a name for the place, the place was whatever you thought it was. Me, I never called it anything but home.

(Abraham's up. Their bed is made of great un-
skinned logs for legs and frame, and half-cut logs
for a headboard. A simple table by the bed is covered with a many-colored silk cloth, with a simple
kerosene lantern, inkwell and old-fashioned nib
pen, neat stack of clean writing paper. Beside
this desk, hand-carved oak bookshelves heavy with
dusty old scrapbooks, leather-bound witchcraft
books, well-stained cook books. Curiosities
abound in the room, though it's plain to see it's a
rude cabin with unvarnished log planks for walls
and young birch trees for joists, and plain square
windows. One wall is entirely covered by a woven
tapestry of many colors, oriental perhaps; Ruth
found it in her Uncle Hymie's house before getting
lost; on the tapestry two horsemen chase a lovely

naked maiden, their arms outstretched to her. She
flees on a white stallion. It is the Rape of
Lucretia or something.

(Abraham turns over and starts a conversation.
His bony lean face is contorted into a funny grim-
ace as his emotions match his narrative. He talks
too much.)

ABRAHAM: Hey Snooker?

*RUTH: Yeah Tootsypie?*

ABRAHAM: Where are we?

*RUTH: We're home, you silly.*

(Ruth is a dark-eyed gypsy girl. She wears a fril-
ly white nightgown, of ancient lace salvaged
from some attic cedar-chest. By day she'd wear
long skirts, wooden shoes, a floppy revealing
blouse [she is full-breasted] and rows and rows of
beads; she'd just take you right in.)

ABRAHAM: Yeah, but I mean where's home, how did we get
here, how long have we been here, etcetera etcetera.

*RUTH: (Mock scorn) What a bunch of dumb questions!*

ABRAHAM: (Giving up) OK so what's on for today?

RUTH: *Well we start with a little oatmeal from the upper pasture (smacking her lips and drawing in closer), some coffee eggs and bacon, then maybe we'll go to Spirit Lake and jump in. Bessie the mooly needs to be fucked by Fergus's bull Freddy. O, and somebody was going out hunting for cinnamon.*

ABRAHAM: (Mock anguish) How can I *choose* from this galaxy of jew-els?

RUTH: *O! and The Fox is supposed to arrive today, if he makes it.*

ABRAHAM: Aw come on since when has The Fox, of all people, not made it?

(Both laugh. They know their friend.)

ABRAHAM: (Sober) You know . . . I was terribly scared last night.

RUTH: *That's only cause you're afraid of your dreams.*

ABRAHAM: Please, you're talking about my inheritance.

RUTH: *You inherited the earth and sky and all the fishies in the stream, what more do you want? (Pause.) Well anyway what did you dream?*

ABRAHAM: O, we were like on this island in the tropics, staying at this incredibly hokey wooden hotel run by an enterprising Chinese family and god knows what we were doing there, it was all vaguely underworld and mysterious, like a tropical detective story. Jacob was there too, and he played his guitar on our balcony overlooking the sea—O and there was one of those slow fans going around on the ceiling and shutters on the windows. I thought you were Ava Gardner and I was Richard Burton in *The Night of the Iguana.*

RUTH: *(Cheerfully) Did you rape me in the surf by moonlight?*

ABRAHAM: (Smiling) Something like that.

RUTH: *You drank too much.*

ABRAHAM: Anise. I was a writer then, we had cockroaches . . .

RUTH: *It was HOT all the time. I wouldn't like that very much. (She issues an involuntary shiver and pulls the covers up to her shoulders)—like to have some good COLD, it stirs up the noodles of your brain.*

ABRAHAM: You're a winter lady, Ruth. The gypsy moth climbs your ladder, eh?

(She pouts, silent and contemplative for a moment, wide huge open eyes staring not at Abraham but straight ahead, expression emotionless.)

ABRAHAM: Penny for your thoughts.

*RUTH: Did you ever read Faulkner?*

ABRAHAM: Not yet.

*RUTH: I wanna have a bumble!*

(Now it is Abraham's turn to stare off, blankly.)

*RUTH: Who will give the faire ladie a bumble?*

ABRAHAM: The Baby Jesus!

*RUTH: (She hits him with her pillow, laughing.) Abraham! I mean it you old . . . pie.*

ABRAHAM: (Now earnest) You'll have a bumble soon enough, don't worry about it. (As an afterthought) Don't worry, be happy.

*RUTH: But I want it now.*

ABRAHAM: Well I'll be your bumble for now, and there's always Theophrastus, the Teddy bear. (Picking up his head, alert) Do you smell coffee perking? Wow, who could be up? You haven't already milked Bessie, have you?

*RUTH: No but Mrs. Lawrence is back you know and she always gets up before dawn to talk to the birds, she says.*

(At this, Abe gets up and hastily pulls on a worn pair of overalls, without underwear. As he begins to leave, Ruth's voice behind him stops him.)

*RUTH: Snooker?*

ABRAHAM: Yeah?

(She says nothing but positions herself on the bed in the pose of a Japanese hostess and noblewoman, sitting on her thigh, with her naked body outstretched and her sweet privates cunningly buried under a long red ostrich feather. Like a painting. She allures him with an eye, but it's an act, a piece of art for his simple entertainment as well. Abraham laughs and turns on his heel, snapping the elastic suspenders of the overalls against his bare chest.)

ABRAHAM: (Muttering to himself) Five planets in Scorpio . . .

(CUT TO the kitchen. Mrs. Lawrence, a portly Irish
lady of 65 years, is over the wood-burning range
with a cotton apron over her florid print dress.
She wears seamed nylon stockings rolled up over
her knees and white nurses' shoes, and a hair net
over her white hair.)

MRS. LAWRENCE: Mustard sandwich, bit o' hot
tea, biscuit, fry 'em over for two!

*RUTH: Mrs. Lawrence, are you the cook today?*

MRS. LAWRENCE: God sent me on this earth to be
a mother to orphans and homosexuals. (She
stares, smiling, at Abraham.) God knows my *own*
children didn't have much of a mother.

ABRAHAM: (Wants to be helpful) Aw, Mrs. Lawrence, let's
just eat breakfast and let the past be over and done with.

MRS. LAWRENCE: (Beaming) You see he's right,
he's my own son!

(The kitchen is also hand-hewn of logs but for the
chimney which rises in its center, which is made
of flat fieldstone mortared tight. Into this
chimney feeds the stove, with black discs for

cooking on its top and an oven. The stove is en-
chanted and heavily ornamented, and has fine iron
angels guarding it on posts on either side. Ord-
inary mudpies of mixed ingredients come out of
this stove as instant decorated chocolate cakes,
peach shortcake with cream, apple pies with fork
impressions around the crust, great heaps of
fish.

(At the far end, a sturdy round table has been
fashioned of a slice of a tree no fewer than six
feet in diameter. This is held up by a center upright log. The table does wobble a bit, though,
tilting toward whoever is monopolizing the conversation at any given time. Eight people could
sit at it comfortably, but now there are only
three, Mrs. Lawrence, Abraham, and Ruth. In the
center of the table a setting holds three round
glass jars with etched glasswork, one says Honey,
the second Molasses, the third Raspberry Pre-
serves. And a bit of salt on a saucer.

(Until The Fox bursts in through the oak Dutch-
door, first opening the bottom half of the door to
reveal bony knees and hairy legs, feet in cheap

shower-thongs of bamboo, emerging from a pin-
stripe pair of Bermuda shorts. The top half of the
door then swings open, revealing the little man
grinning demonically through his squinty small
eyeglasses, and through his Fu Manchu mustache.
His hair is kinky curly, black and wild, rising
six inches off his head, all over his head.)

THE FOX: Now listen this is important. On my way over the gorge
mountain, I noticed somebody left a lot of good old lumber
in a pile. All we gotta do is find a truck somewhere, pick it
up, then we could build a studio and make the movie there,
and . . . Listen, good lumber is getting hard to come by,
do you realize the cost of board lumber in the city has gone
up 100 per cent in the last year alone?

ABRAHAM: We'll have to cut our own at the Spirit Lake mill,
that's all. Can't get it here from the city anyway—

FOX: That's why we need a *truck*. Sometimes I think you're not
*listening* to me.

ABRAHAM: I'm listening, but why do we need to make the
movie anyway?

FOX: Cause we have two alternative routes of getting some
money—we can make the movie or else we can raise and

sell my cucumbers, or we can do both . . . but in either case we need a truck!

ABRAHAM: If we didn't need money, we wouldn't need a truck—we could just hang around!

FOX: (Exasperated by this obviously unrealistic attitude) I'm counting on you to change your mind.

\*          \*          \*

ABRAHAM: Yeah, we'll get it all down, but for the moment how about buckwheat cakes in Bessie butter?

FOX: Far out! (He becomes engrossed in the pancakes, and savors each bite with the exaggerated appreciation of a born ham.)

ABRAHAM: Sure, sure. Today the lower spring, tomorrow the Whole World!

\*          \*          \*

End of Scene Four

SCENE FIVE

(Almost dawn, sky indigo. Camera rests briefly on the red barn in background, and in foreground a 10-foot by 10-foot square house with thick hand-cut pine shingles and a blue peaked roof. Over the roof of this tiny dwelling a copper rooster weathervane tilts in the wind. A sign on the door identifies this as CHEZ POULET.

(Inside the little house, the dawn is shining through a window over Ruth's bed; the window has one pane missing, which is stuffed with a pillow. Ruth beneath several tattered quilts sleeps surrounded by her Teddy bear, assorted books, hot water bottle. Commercial fiberglass building insulation in the roof reads every few feet: "Apply this Side toward Living Space Heated in Winter." Ruth sleeps close to the roof, on a loft over the room. She is dreaming.

(She dreams that Bessie the cow, a Holstein-Jersey, is perched on the sink of a candy soda fountain store in Brooklyn, New York, giving malteds to the kids, among whom is little Ruth, aged five.

One tit gives chocolate, the second vanilla, the
third strawberry, and the last tutti-frutti.

(She re-ignites the fire in a small tin Reeves-
Dover stove, from the coals of the night before.

(The dogs howl because the sun is coming up.)

RUTH: *O Bessie, O Bessie-girl.*

(She warms her hands over the fire, which has
begun to roar, puts on a scarf and exits, saying:)

RUTH: *Today I must get some nails.*

(She steps into the yard in front of the barn. Two
ducks are strutting and quacking about. She stops
in the open door of the outhouse and thrusts her
right arm into it, saying:)

RUTH: *Queen of the outhouse! Out, wench!*

(She pulls Rosemary the white goat from the outhouse, the goat does a double take and prances
off. The sun shines bright on Ruth's wet black
boots as she goes to the well, dips a bucket in,
and carries the water back to the barn and into it.

(She is in Bessie's stall, but the cow is not
there. She removes the cow-pies with a pitchfork,

then spreads straw all over the floor of the
stall.)

RUTH: *Where's Bess? Where's my girl?*

(She watches at the door while Bessie finishes her
breakfast of apples and rosehips in the pasture.
Bessie then slowly approaches as Ruth coos.

(She sings her favorite milking song while
milking, to the background of squirting milk Ping
Ping.)

RUTH: *(Singing)*
*If you don't love me*
*Love who you please*
*Wrap your arms around me*
*Give my heart ease.*

(She hums the last verses, gets up from her stool,
notices Bessie's tail is sticking straight out,
walks behind the cow to examine her privates. It's
time.)

RUTH: *Well Bess it's your time all right. Shall I walk you down*
*to Ferguson's bull? (Brushing the cow.) Gonna go*
*a-courting? You gotta look bright-eyed, girl. Don't want*
*anything too badly to be neighborly, and stand for him.*

(She mutters to herself as she exits with the milkpail.

(CUT TO Ruth, Bessie and Yale, a clean-cropped young man in jeans, flannel shirt and bright red bandana. With them is Clambone, a mixed-breed yellow dog.)

*RUTH: Yale, you'll have to ask him. Fergus makes me feel like a schoolmarm.*

YALE: Well I'll handle it. If it comes to it I'll give him a pint.

*RUTH: Fergus might do it himself for a fifth!*

YALE: (Proudly) So might any drinkingman!

(CUT TO the barnyard at Ferguson's place. This, clearly, is civilization; there's some rural mailboxes, a few old cars, even a lonely telephone-and-electricity wire . . . It's a dairy farm with many cows, many children, and one fine bull. Ferguson's wife is on the porch plucking a chicken, and her only acknowledgment of the arrival of Yale, Ruth and Bessie is a hostile grunt.

(Fergus himself is about 50 years old, a few teeth missing, great strong arms, balding with short

hair behind. He and his kin are, in fact, the
natives of the area.)

YALE: Fergus! How're ya doin?

FERGUS: *Not bad.*

YALE: Listen, we got a little cow here needs your help. You
got a bull that can fuck 'er?

FERGUS: *Watch your mouth, boy, there's women here.
(Eyes Ruth greedily.)*

RUTH: *Yeah? Where the fuck are they?*

YALE: (Barely suppressing a grin) And this is the milkmaid.

RUTH: *(Shyly) I'm not sure she's in heat, but she's acting all
funny and holding her tail straight out.*

(Fergus walks from yard to road, hands square on
his hips. Camera pans the field as all the cows
turn their heads.)

FERGUS: *Boy! Boy! Come boy! Come boy! (He shouts
Boy! so loudly that the hills echo it back to him, and
so shrilly that it sounds like "Bye, Bye.")*

(The scene is very still, shifting to the mythic.

The bull comes along followed by three young blond-headed boys with switches.

(CUT TO Chez Poulet, Ruth's little cabin, where the scene opened. Ruth is recounting the story of Fergus and the bull to Abraham, who's calmly whittling a stick with his jackknife. As she speaks, the image flashes back to the scene she describes, soundlessly.)

RUTH: *Fergus was standing in the middle of the hollow when the bull came sullen to meet him. He tried to rope the ring through the bull's nose, you know, and watching them I thought well Fergus has met his match. They were two of the same.*

(IMAGE: Fergus and the bull in a fierce ballet, Fergus trying to rope the bull's nose and the bull struggling away. Finally, he is subdued and, with blood dripping from his nose, climbs aboard Fergus' old cattle truck. Sympathy shifts to bull, and mythic cadence gives way to slapstick.)

RUTH: *He didn't want her. It wasn't time yet. I had to leave Bessie down at Fergus'.*

ABRAHAM: Well I couldn't wrestle no old bull to the ground, and I can't give Bessie a baby either.

(Ruth picks up a red shawl, wraps it around her shoulders coquettishly and shakes it in front of Abraham, halfway between a matador and a washerwoman.)

RUTH: *Boy! Boy! Come boy! Come boy!*

(She ascends the ladder to her loft. Abraham at first refuses to be amused, but gradually succumbs and follows her up.

(CUT TO Fergus' yard again. The bull is lustily having his way with our Bessie. Fergus stands behind them grinning from ear to ear.)

FERGUS: *He's gettin' her good! He's gettin' her good!*

\*        \*        \*

End of Scene Five

SCENE SIX

(Abe walking down a dirt path, the trail is leafy,
large trees overhang everywhere, yet the sunlight
comes through bright. Abe comes upon a crudely
lettered sign, THIS WAY TO SILENT'S HOUSE. He follows it a bit further and comes to a strange little
hut, sort of an A-frame; only the main floor is dug
out, one step down as you enter. The roof of the
hut is sod, wild weeds and strange shrubbery are
sticking out in every direction; perhaps it's a
reflection of the mountain of curly hair all over
Silent's head, he now standing in front the house
and waving to Abe coming down the path. The sound
of dogs barking is everywhere.

(Abraham approaches Silent who is perhaps twenty
years old, though his face has strange lines like
curlicues in it; in fact, these lines, mostly from
grinning which Silent does constantly, these
curly lines are reflections of his curly hair.
Silent is Harpo Marx of the New Age; but where
Harpo made us roll over with slapstick and
graceful though mock clumsiness, Silent is more
subtle, a mime artist par excellence. He makes us

54

laugh with the slightest of movements, a finger
scratching a solitary follicle of hair, an
eyebrow raised in such a manner, etc. Silent wears
a thick-furred Afghani vest, a brilliant white
fur-color and under it a wine-red turtleneck; his
pants are more pantaloons, cossack-style perhaps, but patched by none-other-than Silent himself, a quite nimble tailor. He wears high boots,
the pants bloop out at the knee.)

ABRAHAM: (Now just a few yards from where Silent stands,
broom in hand) Hello . . . my name's Abe . . . I'm a
friend of Ruth's, you know, with the dark hair. (Abraham
talks very slowly, enunciating each word with care, like
one talking to a foreigner, or someone with a speech
defect. Abraham knows that Silent never speaks; they
aren't sure whether he is able to or not, he never does;
Ruth has told this to Abe and now he speaks very slowly,
over-conscious of his own ability to make words and
sentences.)

(Dogs barking now coming from either inside the
house, or from behind it.)

ABRAHAM: Ruth, she said you had a dog, some people left it
when they migrated to the southland, a white dog she said

it was, and big. (He has been speaking slowly, now waits patiently, Abe thinking that it takes Silent a lot of time to digest what he's just said.)

SILENT: *(Smiles at Abe, nods his head, yes, yes, spreads his hands wide, a big dog, and from nowhere—for Silent is also a sleight-of-hand magician, like his predecessor—a tapemeasure, one of those with a spring which draws the tape in with a snap, this tape measure is in Silent's palm and he measures from the ground up to the height of the dog, whom we hear barking in the background.)*

ABRAHAM: (Smiling now, as is Silent) I always did want a big dog, and I guess I'm going to be here for a while.

SILENT: *(Claps his hands together with a nice crack!, does a little dance and then goes over to a small trap-front door on the side of his house. He opens it and out comes the mushking dog, Mamoushka, an Alaskan Samoyed with thick fur, white and pure as the driven snow and then some. Mamoushka's eyes are brown-yellow, she runs up to Silent who bends down to hug her, then looks up at Abe standing and watching and Silent points once to Abe then to the dog. Silent takes the broom which he was leaning on earlier and begins to write in the sand-dirt in front of his house: he writes the word Mamoushka. Abraham says it over once, then louder, he calls the dog over and she comes to him as natural as you would have it.)*

ABRAHAM: She's so beautiful, wow! Oh Silent, she's too much! (He hugs the dog, pats her on the top of the head.) Wait till Ruthie sees her, I've got to get back soon. (He starts to get ready to walk back toward the main houses but Silent puts on a mock stern face and motions Abe to hold it a minute, Silent now like a Keystone-comedy cop flat palm held up facing Abe: then Silent steps back to the trap door and opens it, three black and white puppies, clearly Mamoushka's, come dancing out.)

(The light bulb goes on) I get it, the puppies come with, four for the price of one, what a deal! (Truly joyous, it is a great deal) .

*SILENT: (Holds up one of the puppies, all black but with white feet in front, and motions that it is his, but that Abe is to take the rest. Abe acknowledges, calls to Mamoushka and they start down the trail once again, Abraham, the big white dog and two of the puppies.)*

\* \* \*

End of Scene Six

## SCENE SEVEN

(Back in the kitchen. Abraham, Ruth, and The Fox
are at the round table drinking coffee in earthen
mugs from an old tin coffeepot. Mamoushka stands
alert for leftover bits of cinnamon biscuits. The
kitchen has changed, only the stove and the chimney are the same. It has become the Cafe Depresso,
with a racy calendar on the wall (flip the plastic
cover and the Liz Taylor-look-alike is nekid) and
a multi-colored paper balloon lampshade, candle
in a wine bottle and French music.)

THE FOX: (Still excited) When the cucumbers are ready we got to
set up a smooth all-day production operation else we can't
get all the pickles done before the tomatoes start.

*RUTH: (Far-away) Eggplant! (ecstatic) Zucchini!*

ABRAHAM: O, don't worry . . . we'll get whatever the Good
Lord sends us . . . (smiling, he dons his dark glasses
again, it's Paris beatniks in the 1920s).

FOX: (Still serious, intense) No, wait, if there's too much food
we'll just ask the Spirit Lake people to come up here and

help . . . they could share the crop, and with that kind of *labor force* . . .

ABRAHAM: (A public announcement to a make-believe audience) The Fox has promised cucumbers to feed the entire kingdom! By appointment to the realm, bread-and-butter pickles for a thousand years! (The rest applaud.)

FOX: (Triumphant) We'll see who plays in the winter game!

ABRAHAM: (Musing) Well, you never know.

*RUTH: (Sincerely and sweetly) We must play fools, and we must play well. For if we amuse the king he will spare us.*

ABRAHAM: (From behind dark glasses and a cigarette) You mean we're essentially in show business?

*RUTH: You said it, boy. On with the show!*

ABRAHAM: But where's the audience?

*RUTH: (In a whisper, as if He must not hear) The king.*

FOX, ABRAHAM: (Together) Long love the king!

FOX: (Under his breath) The king is dead. The fish must die.

*RUTH: (Returning to the subject) We're in show business just because we're public entertainers—that's our contribution,*

*silly. We're not very good farmers, right, so we're not feeding the hungry mouths of Asia or anything; and we're not armed revolutionaries or rich businessmen or scientists or teachers. We're* clowns.

FOX: Funny, I was just thinking this was a scene from *Hernando's Hideaway.*

ABRAHAM: Funny, *I* thought it was a Tibetan monastery . . .

FOX: Don't confuse the issue, we need some nice LSD!

(Abraham and Ruth react simultaneously with a sigh. Alas, no LSD in sight.

(Mrs. Lawrence enters in a clean apron worn over the same dirty dress, her only dress, and the same nurse's shoes.)

MRS. LAWRENCE: LSD doesn't grow on trees, y'know. Meantime, you might try some corn-on-the-cob. It's pretty trippy, haw haw! (She pokes Abraham in the ribs.) Careful, it's hot.

(She places a steaming platter of corn-on-the-cob before them, and a small earthen pot containing butter.)

MRS. LAWRENCE: There's some of Yale's beer on the porch that I cooled up in the stream, but leave some for tonight, hey (poking Abraham again) I figure I'm old enough to drink two or three of a summer evening—haw haw—

ABRAHAM: (Delirious) Stop! Stop! It's blowing my mind!

(Quick cut to autumn wind blowing outside, trees swaying, overall view of town square, three out-buildings, two houses, a barn, a patch of green in front of the house: we hear the wind, then

(CUT TO Dutch-door of Cafe Depresso, which we left only a second ago for the outdoor shot, and the candle on the table blows out. Enter John, tall and thin, wearing thick rimless spectacles, un-shaven, 30 years old, British accent, tousled brown curly hair, wearing red white and blue bell-bottoms and an outlandish belt and buckle, and a cloth vest. Enter with him Jacob, who's younger, shorter, heavier, he's a gone angel of rough stuff, wears a felt hat bashed in on top, bright red shirt, green work pants or jeans, and boots. His tough-guy exterior soon becomes like a joke, a parody in which Jake himself partakes: nobody is intimidated, rather they laugh and embrace him,

he's like a little kid who needs a shave. These two
are the ambassadors of the Spirit Lake people,
they live in the village, down the road a ways.)

JOHN: (Wagging his finger at the assembly; in heavy
British accent) There's no patching up blown
minds, you know! (All laugh heartily.)

ABRAHAM: (Joking) Are you still good for nothing, John?

JOHN: That's just what I'm good for but I haven't
seen it yet—there's too much of everything
already, have you seen the corn? (Doesn't wait
for reply.) Well, it's almost ready! Besides, I've
been practising.

ABE: Your guitar?

JOHN: Banjo.

JACOB: (Sees his entrance, calmly but slyly) Say, did I tell you
what the trees said? (All are suddenly focused on this
point.) Miss Moonbeam's going to drop a baby boychild
on Hallowe'en.

JOHN: (Scratching his head) I knew I'd forgotten the
message . . .

(Ruth shrieks with hysterical joy, clapping her

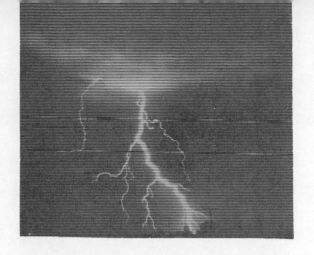

hands and dancing a little jig. She is beaming and
even The Fox exudes a quiet, I-knew-it-all-the-
time contentment.)

JACOB: *(Adopting true ambassadorial posture, he sweeps his
hat to his knees and bows low.) Thus we bring our
finest harvest to grace such a table as yours.*

THE FOX: (Enthused) The alliance between the Spirit Lake people
and the Family of Sometime will outlast the end of
times . . .

*RUTH: (In loving admonishment) O don't be so silly dogmatic
about it. (They both laugh.)*

THE FOX: You're a dog-ma! (Points to Ruth's lap where
Mamoushka lays her head in the checkered apron.)

JACOB: *(His grandest gesture) And you're all invited to the
Sagittarian Bash. Everyone you know will be there, right
after Harvest!*

(CUT TO the face of The Fox, smiles discreetly and
nothing says. A sudden darkness in the room is
followed by a tremendous thunderclap and the
sound of rain whipping the cottage walls and
windows.)

*RUTH: (Jumping up alarmed) O! my bread!! (She races out the door.)*

JOHN: (To Jacob) Was she baking her bread *outside*?

(Jacob shrugs his shoulders, he doesn't know. He puts his hat back on, slaps his thigh and collapses into a chair at the table, laughing. John, still standing, appears in a daze, or a dream. Abraham lopes over to the Dutch-doors, and exits. Camera follows him onto a long porch on which are three old rocking chairs, one bicycle, a table full of old books and crayons, a pitcher on the sill. The rain pours down, dripping over the edge of the porch roof.

(Abraham, and we, can see Ruth scampering about the yard clutching tins full of yeasty dough which she had left rising on top of a large stone fireplace with metal grill, very homemade-makeshift. Beyond her the rain falls clear up over a long open hill up to a neat round orchard backed by the forest-line which forms a heavy wall of green. It is Abe's perspective at the end of Scene Three, his first view of the town from the top of the hill, only precisely reversed this time, from the porch of the house looking up toward the top of

the hill. In the yard Mamoushka and three puppies
are running around and two ducks, Alphonse and
Gaston, both white with pink beaks and legs,
quacking happily, they're water fowl after all.
But the goat, Rosemary, has taken the porch as
refuge from the storm, she cowers in one corner,
behind a rocker and protected by the porch tar-
paper roof; Rosemary is bleating softly.)

*        *        *

End of Scene Seven

## SCENE EIGHT

(A beautiful rainbow from the storm. The air is
bright and clear. We're in the garden.

(The garden is tall with corn, early sweet corn,
August corn, with golden tassles and thick with
knee-high greens signifying carrots, tomatoes,
potatoes, squash.

(SOUND: The Incredible String Band singing
"'Greatest Friend.'"

(Camera looks down a long row of vegetables and
comes to close-up of a hoe pulling weeds from the
row of potatoes. At the end of the hoe is Abraham.
He lets the tool drop and gets down on hands and
knees, pulling at the weeds every which way. After
a few minutes his attention is distracted by Bessie the Cow, who pokes her face at him through a
row of corn. Bessie is wearing a collar and brass
bell around her neck. Short behind her, and driving her with a little clean stick, is Ruth, dark-
eyed among the corn. She's sort of admonishing

Bessie, the corn after all is not for the cow-
ladies. Ruth is barefoot and wears a colorful thin
cotton dress which comes to just below the knee.

(She and Abraham lie down in the field and make
love between the rows of omniscient trustworthy
vegetables. Looking down the field we can see two
or three other kids sitting under a tree, talking,
taking a break perhaps from their work in the garden. Now we come back to Abraham and Ruth, their
love and orgasm has a childlike delight and in-
nocence to it, they are both embarrassed, for ex-
ample. The camera reveals all that it can see of
this love, while the song continues in the background. The song ends on a lazy harmonica note,
the sun is hot, the lovers fall asleep.)


### GREATEST FRIEND
Mike Heron


The greatest friend I have in life
has brought me here to dwell
Awhile among your green green hills
All by the watery well
The water from that wondrous well

has made my eyes to see
And loosed my tongue to sing with joy
That such a friend can be.

The greatest friend I have in life
was hidden long from me
Above the mountains cold and wide
beneath the sacred tree
That sacred tree whose bark i touched
whose leaves did tell to me
the ancient tales that made me sure
my friend would come to me.

My greatest friend a song has given
to sing where i may go
to sing among the green green hills
and where the waters flow
the waters from that wondrous well
that made my eyes to see
and made my mind to ever show
my greatest friend to me.

*       *       *

End of Scene Eight

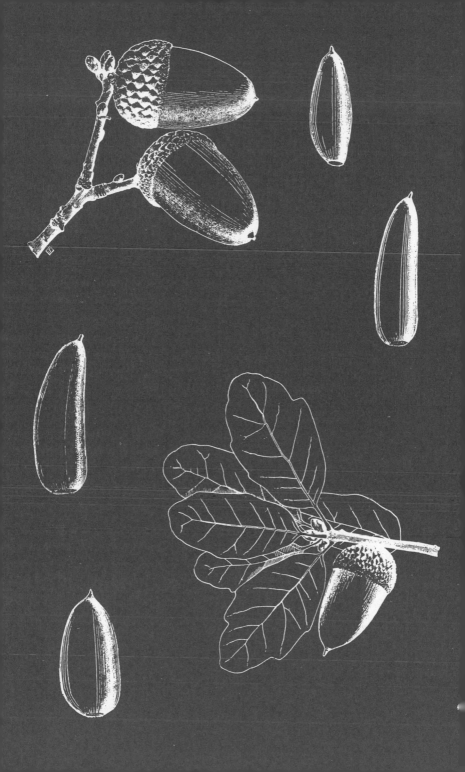

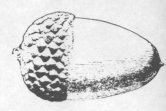

### SCENE NINE

(<u>Mad John</u> from Scene Seven and <u>Wonderboy</u> are walking down a dirt road through the maple forest.
John is dressed as before, an inept homemade rock-
n-roll star, "not commercial," and Wonderboy
wears an Indian shirt, shorts, and sandals. He is
blond and about 16.)

JOHN: (Animated) So tell me Wonderboy what do
you have in your pouch there?

(Points to a leather pouch hanging from Wonderboy's waist.)

WONDERBOY: (Cheerfully) Acorns!

JOHN: What's them good for?

WONDERBOY: You use 'em to make tannic acid. It's
good for dyeing.

JOHN: (Startled) Dying!

WONDERBOY: (Innocent of the pun) Yeah, like
clothes and things.

JOHN: And how do you fix the freezer?

*WONDERBOY: O Buzzy can get a relay from the dump.*

JOHN: Of course! From the dump!

(It is in the nature of Wonderboy to know everything about practical skills. One speaks to him not of love and soul, but of woodcarving, mountain-climbing and canoe-building. But his eyes reveal a complete appreciation of the magic.)

*WONDERBOY: Anyway, we haven't got a freezer. Boy, I'd like to climb that old tree someday and set up like a rope ride from the top of it down to the top of the old maple yonder in the field (motioning)—ha—like Tarzan or somethin', boy.*

(Wonderboy, seen full front, is wearing a simple cotton T-shirt on which someone has embroidered a flagrant green "W."

JOHN: Did you hear something?

(Both listen. A certain faint creaking, as of a wagon and team approaching.)

*WONDERBOY: Indians. (Lowering his voice) I know a*

*place where we can see 'em without scarin' 'em off. We can just look at 'em go by.*

JOHN: (Also whispering) Let's go!

(They duck off the road and climb into the hollowed-out trunk of a gigantic old elm tree. There they await the Indians.)

JOHN: Are the Indians around here friendly?

*WONDERBOY: I don't know. I never met one. I guess they sure must be friendly. They don't come around. Shh!*

(What is passing is no Indian wagon-train, but a circus wagon, complete but for the elephant, being hauled by two funny donkeys. There's a silhouette of a fat driver, rather jolly, but no conversation. From the back of the wagon comes calliope music, high-pitched and gay, tooting the melody of the song "You Are My Sunshine.")

JOHN: Circus coming to town?

*WONDERBOY: Fen of Wick's Travelling Zoo, I think.*

JOHN: O, is that all?

WONDERBOY: (Like a disappointed freckled kid) Yeah.

JOHN: Are you sure? (His tone and the look in his eye are playfully sinister.) Nothing to hide?

> (Wonderboy cuts off onto an old woods trail to the left of the road, chooses a familiar fat maple and climbs its lower limbs, then hangs from the bottom limb upside-down from his knees. John watches merrily. Wonderboy falls from the tree, rolls over on his back on the leafy ground with perfect agility, bounds upright again.)

WONDERBOY: Come on, we'll save a mile to the lake this way.

> (They disappear. Out of another dirt trail, to the right of the road, come Ruth and Moonbeam, who is very pregnant, and Silent, who has one of them on each arm. Ruth and Moonbeam are both wearing patchwork multicolored cotton frocks down to their ankles, but with generous open necks, and sandals. Silent is all decked out in nautical blues, bellbottom bluejeans over his sparkling white sneakers with green undersides, a zig-zag pattern red and white T-shirt, and a stiff white sailor's cap on top of his curls.)

MOONBEAM: *(Walking down the road) I don't even know if I can still go swimming with this one kicking around! (She pats her belly with both hands; it is truly enormous.)*

(Moonbeam has long jet-black hair and black eyes, but her cheeks are glowing red.

(Silent shapes an elegant schooner with his hands and does a little deck-rolling shuffle, indicating he will build Moonbeam a boat and they can take a cruise on Spirit Lake without even getting wet.)

MOONBEAM: *Right! A boat is what we need!*

**RUTH: *If you wrap my throat in seaweed, I will sing you rocks and shipwrecks . . .***

MOONBEAM: *We'd have two of everything and just float off to the Singing Islands.*

**RUTH: *(Clearly enjoys the fantasy for a moment, then stops short gulping with surprise realization) But what about Rosemary and Bessie? There's only one of them!***

MOONBEAM: *O gosh I'm sorry, we'll just have to get another cow and a goat!*

RUTH: O, of course! Bessie's baby should be a boy, then we'd be all set!

MOONBEAM: (Serious, now, and playful) When you gonna have a baby, Ruth?

RUTH: (Far-away) O I had twins once . . .

(There's an embarrassed pause for a moment, then Moonbeam is ready to cheer her up.)

MOONBEAM: Well listen if I have twins you can have one of them!

RUTH: Really??

MOONBEAM: Well, sure! (Wait: she's not sure.) If there's two of them, I'll have one to spare! (She's not sure.) Anyway it won't go very far away from home! (She's sure.)

(Ruth eeks and shrieks, hugs and kisses Moonbeam, who embraces her.)

RUTH: Wait till I tell Abe about this!

(At this, they arrive at a T in the road, that's where you can go either right or left, but not straight ahead. There's an old stone fence and wall of spruce trees forming the T and a gaudy hurdy-gurdy gone Peanut Wagon with circus wheels and a little tin chimney of stovepipe wearing a cap. A team of donkeys wearing red felt hats (slits for their ears) is hitched to the wagon and Abraham, dressed now in gypsy runaway outfit with bandana and boots, is the driver. With him are The Fox, naked but for a pair of shower-thongs on his feet, and Uncle Louie, who is very fat, about 300 pounds, has long black curly hair and a bushy mustache, is about 38 years old, wears green striped trousers held up by a super pair of red suspenders. He carries a gallon jug of wine. All are smiling, as if in anticipation of the girls and Silent. A crude sign, black paint on white birchbark, says SPIRIT LAKE with an arrow to the East.)

ABRAHAM: Tell Abe about what?

(Mamoushka appears from within the wagon, acknowledges the scene, and retreats.)

RUTH: *About summer turning to fall and cold nights in the chicken house with winter breathing hard and barren behind me.*

UNCLE LOUIE: *Winter! Ha! Ha! Ha! Why winter won't be*

*for ages yet, my dear girl. We're going swimming at Spirit Lake right now, if you'd like to ride in our humble cart.*

(Silent hasn't waited to be invited, jumps on the back of the wagon, throwing off the canvas covering to reveal a little tea-table room within, with the dogs lying about on throw rugs and a small black-mahogany round table set for tea for three with teapot, cups and scones steaming on a plate, and butter. Silent, Ruth, and Moonbeam are seated around the table as the cart pulls off. On the wall between driver and cargo, an embroidered framed plaque: "God is our Refuge and Strength."

FOX: (Taking off) You know I think we've got the thing all set up now . . . (inhales a blue cigarette). Yes now we're in no danger, everything's fine . . .

(The peanut wagon is gone.

(Late afternoon sunshine beaming through the great silent forest on a gleaming brook beyond the T in the road. Fergus appears momently from behind a big sycamore, looks around furtively.)

*FERGUS: Whatdya suppose they're up to?*

(Vanishes again as he hears voices. It's Jacob and
Marie, a lean and beautiful foreigner perhaps 25
years old. He's a woodsman and she a queen. He's in
leather, she's in colorful wools. They come from
the right half of the T, from the direction opposite Spirit Lake, that is from Baby Farm, and
turn towards Spirit Lake.)

MARIE: *And tell me Jacob (she pronounces it "Jaaa-Kob"),
what are your people, this people of Spirit Lake, like?
They are good ones? (Touching his arm.)*

JACOB: O, just as good as you think.

MARIE: *(Pleased) O I like that. We are whatever the ozzer
one think we are, so we live to help the ozzer one . . .*

JACOB: (Perplexed by the sudden philosophy) No I just mean
these people came together for some unknowable but
pure motivation. So they make a life of it together.
There's no problem.

MARIE: *(Delighted) Pas de problemes! C'est merveilleux!
Abraham (She pronounces it "Ab-rahm") has told me of
your wonderful (searching for the word) horses there; he
said "Watch out for Jacob's horses," they are yours?*

JACOB: Ha! No, it's just an old saying. Actually I don't have

any horses right now. Or at least I don't know that I've got 'em yet.

MARIE: *Well that's funny . . . I think that you had the horses yourself, from what I have heard of Abraham.*

JACOB: (Softly) No. Nope.

MARIE: *Jacob?*

JACOB: Yes?

MARIE: *I love you.*

JACOB: (Pleased) And what about Abraham?

MARIE: *It's simple, I love him too!*

JACOB: And do you love us together or separately! (Laughing, it's a game now.)

MARIE: *I think (coy)—togezzer!*

JACOB: (A little embarrassed, he changes the subject) Well, everybody's gonna be at the lake goin' swimmin, soon it'll be fall and too cold, it's August already and by Jesus June was just yesterday.

(And at this the lake appears at the foot of the hill, it's set as in a gorge, fresh gurgling water surrounded by steep slate and granite cliffs. There's a small ten-foot waterfall which you can tumble over on your bottom; and there's an ancient covered bridge, once stained red, which spans the gorge 40 feet over the water. From this bridge the bravest of the villagers jump, feet first, and make a tremendous splash below. About 50 people are gathered here and there about the lake, some swimming, others cooking up a roast, still others lying in the sun, which shows the forest's green marred by a tint of yellow on its edges and once again the wind.)

\*       \*       \*

End of Scene Nine

SCENE TEN

(IMAGE: Spirit Lake. The waterfall turns a water
wheel which powers a mill. The people live in the
mill also, some of them; the upper floors of the
mill have windows, open, with checkered curtains.
Some folks are swimming bare-ass, others prepar-
ing a harvest feast. The grass is golden in color
and texture. Everybody we've already met is
there.)

NARRATOR'S VOICE: Summer was the best time for
beginning, everything grew then and even the mountain
was pregnant with promise for the future. The Fox became
our titular leader, and traveled from Mrs. Lawrence's
house to Spirit Lake to Silent's and Ferguson's and even
all the way to the family known as Mandrake Plains. We
all enjoyed his posture, but none of us felt *led* by him, he
was just one of several strains holding the piece together.

(IMAGE: Camera follows The Fox around the prem-
ises, he's still naked, he talks incessantly,
patting this one on the shoulder and embracing the
other one, kissing a baby. He's a regular magic

politician. If he crossed his legs and spread his arms, he'd be Christ.)

NARRATOR'S VOICE: Somehow the place became home, and all the safe kitchens of our parents' houses were at unimaginable distances. The Fox coordinated the building of houses, reaping of garden harvests and the delicate house-of-cards construction of love affairs. It was he who found Moonbeam her midnight youth, and encouraged her baby.

(IMAGE: The vastly pregnant Moonbeam sits peeling apples while Wonderboy, at her side, brushes her hair with a fistful of spruce twigs. She catches the parings in her apron.)

NARRATOR'S VOICE: Sometimes The Fox went too far, and for building a house of cards in one place, he managed to tear one down somewhere else.

(IMAGE: Marie, bathing. She swims languidly from a tree stump which sticks out three feet over the water level in the middle of the lake, to the shore. She sits on a rock drying off and looking at the lake as people look at oceans, she yearns for her far-away homeland perhaps. She seems alone,

feels lost and insecure, forces a brave smile
anyway.)

NARRATOR'S VOICE: Summer was the best time for
beginning because nobody noticed the time passing until it
was fall. It was always light and dreamy, it's hard to
believe it was like that, but it's true. The earth itself gave
up treasures without end in those summer days. Corn,
peaches. It was an easy time in the houses, too. Nobody
noticed that The Fox never built a house for himself to
live in, only for others, he had no lovers. It got tense. Fall
came.

(IMAGE: The Fox has settled down onto a Moroccan
throw rug on the ground with Abraham and Ruth.
Behind them, a volleyball game is in progress. One
team wears red jerseys and the other blue, all
wear bright white birchbark slippers. A sign on a
nearby tree reads "Intramurals." Abe and Ruth
have set out a neat picnic lunch, with chicken
legs.)

FOX: I think it's all set up now, we're finally into the rhythm of
the place. It's almost time for me to leave.

ABE: Where you going?

FOX: Cuba, I think.

ABE: (Dazzled by the very notion) Cuba? What's down there? Anyway you can't get there from here.

FOX: (Dead serious) Listen, the Cuban social experiment is important, it could mean some changes around here in the near future . . .

ABE: (Interrupting, laughing) You think the changes around here haven't been incredible enough already? Brother, I'm half-dead from keepin' up with the changes around here. (Nods his head, laughs again.)

FOX: (Undeterred) Around here, certainly, but matters are largely the same in the greater society around us.

ABE: (Challenging) How do *you* know?

FOX: What?

ABE: How do *you* know?

FOX: (Momentarily silent) It's obvious. Look at the colleges! Look at the elections!

ABE: (Leaping up, triumphant) *Where are they?*

(Sure enough they are nowhere to be seen. A moment

of silence, then the game is over and the masques
are dropped.)

ABE: Foxhall Foxcraft what can I do to ease your mind?

FOX: Take my body and throw it away, it aches all over from
napalm and TV Guide.

ABE: Take your body and keep it warm!

FOX: (Defensive, he spurns Abraham's open arms) Stop it. It's too
beautiful. It's too perfect.

ABE: And *you* made it so. So?

FOX: So.

*RUTH: You can't reform the Eskimos! (Smiles, as if she'd
solved the problem. The Fox returns her smile, but thinly.)*

ABE: Well if you really go to Cuba you'll be further away than
the moon.

FOX: And close as frost.

(They lunge for each other and embrace . . .

(Dogs barking. A great stirring at the center of
the meadow, where a bright canopy has been erected
and under it, tables heavy with food. There are
bowls of corn-on-the-cob steaming hot, trays of

fish, peas, beans, voluminous salads of tomatoes and greens, warm bread on wooden slicing boards with knives, tall pitchers of beer, triangular blocks of cheddar cheese, open blueberry pies, etc. etc. All converge on the spot.

(They perform a graceful ritual dance about the canopy, called a Pleasure Dome, to harvest-music. All change partners. It's like a Maypole, but with fruit and produce. It's elaborate and erotic.

(A cloudburst darkens the sky and a sudden rainfall begins. All scurry under the Pleasure Dome for protection, forming a tight knot within it. The mood is gay and cheerful despite the rain, and one by one they emerge from the Dome, a change of heart, and welcome the rain all over their bodies, rubbing and stroking it on.)

*     *     *

End of Scene Ten

L. JOHNSON & CO

## SCENE ELEVEN

(IMAGE: Back at the village now, the house and porch in background, orange pumpkins on the porch railings; the woodshed is in the foreground. The woodshed is the exclusive province of Wonderboy, who stands at ease with an axe alongside a heavy elm stump (chopping-block). In the corner, a rustic bed set on fieldstone supports, work tables strewn with hand tools: two-man crossbuck saw, wooden hammers with flint heads, a fro, some saws, chisels, some hatchets, a machete, two or three shovels, pickaxe, rake, broom made of straws bound to a slender young birch, hoe, simple wheelbarrow. Walls are lined with cut and stacked cords of hardwoods for winter and kitchen fuel.

(It's more like fall than summer. The harvest-dance was the last song of summer. Now the leaves are bright red, orange and yellow and strewn about the green ground where they have fallen from the trees. Our friends are dressed more warmly, in bright flannel shirts, scarves, knit caps, strong boots. The wind is never quite silent.

(In the woodshed are Wonderboy, the unbearded

youth-host, The Fox, Ruth, and two lieutenants of
the army called Mandrake Plains. An animated
conversation.)

***RUTH: Where're you fellas from?***

TOM: I'm Tom, this is Richard, we're from Mandrake Plains.

(Tom and Richard are very young, surely not beyond
their teens, and yet clearly possessed of some
spirit or other. There is a deliberate and careful
manner to their speech. Their eyes sparkle. They
are messengers of a certain god. Though young and
badly schooled, they are thoroughly professional
and self-assured about their religion. They are
more stereotypically hippie than our other
friends, their hair is much longer and they wear
beads, bellbottom jeans, etc.)

**FOX: Ah! And how are things over the mountain at your place?**

TOM: (Nervously) O fine, fine, couldn't be better, we got a pretty big
group now, 250 or so.

**FOX: (Astounded, fearful) That many?**

TOM: O yes, there's no stopping the Lord's word once the people get
free wind of it! (He pauses, swallowing and maintaining a

frozen grin during the pitch.) Say, can it be YOU don't hear the Lord's voice?

FOX: How do you mean?

(The Fox knows exactly what Tom means, and mumbles this last almost to himself and staring at the ground.)

TOM: Well the Lord's among us you know. He's our avatar and father. And he's not far from you, just over the mountain and behind your decadent life. Think about it, and give yourself to Him.

RICHARD: At Mandrake Plains, we neither smoke nor drink nor fornicate without the Lord's blessing in marriage. Those are the rules. If you expect to get . . . HIGHER . . . you got to recognize that power that's greater than all of us together. . . .

(Richard can't quite see. He squints and draws up practically nose-to-nose to The Fox to make his point.)

FOX: Well there's a power, or a discipline, that's greater than all of us put together—but we don't have to *recognize* it, I mean we couldn't *not* recognize it, it's just us, we are it. We

couldn't be wrong, or out of it, whatever we are is what it is.

"Telling us to be pure would be like telling water to be wet," I think Ramakrishna said that.

*RUTH: Kerouac. Kerouac said that.*

FOX: Yes. In the Scripture of the Golden Eternity. So you see, friends, the world has a discipline and we're part of it and any discipline we cultivate within ourselves would be vanity. (To Ruth) Did I do good?

*RUTH: (Laughing, it's all a game) You done good. (Leaning against the woodpile, nonchalant) Funny . . . I saw some of your brothers smoking down in the graveyard just yesterday (laughs innocently, the joke's on them).*

TOM: (Snapping) It couldn't be true.

FOX: (A rare pose, the peace-maker) Well the Lord is a mighty fellow and I'm sure he's got room for all of us.

TOM: (Unplacated) It's easy for you to say that! Say anything you want, it's easier than changing your life, the bad vibrations from this settlement are making our full elevation on this mountain impossible. You guys, you faithless ones, you'll find you can only stand in the Lord's way so long . . .

RUTH: *(Up for the fight) If the Lord is just Gregory, you bring him over here, I'll talk some sense into him!*

RICHARD: (Stuttering now in outrage) G-G-Gregory was born to lead men out of sin and into the neo-Atlantan Age.

RUTH: *Gregory was born, about 17 years ago, to be a farmboy, and instead got to be a messiah to confused lost children.*

WONDERBOY: *(Sighing, he's not much for arguments) 'Twas ever thus!*

TOM: You'll hear more of us on the airwaves. Don't think you can laugh and live in sin here forever! Moral pollutants!

(Exit Richard and Tom, the latter leading the former by the arm.)

FOX: (Obviously agitated by the interview) Well! *Fuck them!* That's all, just fuck 'em!

RUTH: *O, take it easy. They're just a bunch of kids.*

FOX: Bunch of kids who want to take over all we've built here for joy and peace for their shitty little guru and his harem.

RUTH: *(Wide-eyed) Really? I thought Gregory only had one woman at a time.*

FOX: What's the difference? That bastard's no kid, Ruth; what we've got here is the Hitler youth! 250 of them! No fornication! Them's the rules! God I fled America in my youth to get away from rules!

RUTH: *(Still refusing to see the seriousness of the situation) Why, Fox, are you afraid they'll come here to spoil my virtue?*

FOX: (Even he has to laugh at the idea.) Aw, you're different.

RUTH: *Just cause I'm Jewish?*

WONDERBOY: *(From the corner of the room, where he's tooling legs for a bench) What?*

FOX: No, just cause you can take care of yourself.

RUTH: *I can take care of you too. Now forget the Mandrake Plains and their cosmic comprehension. Last year, it was the old people who were coming to get us, this year it's the children—what are you, twenty-five? What's the use? What's the use, Fox? What comes to get us just comes, and not before. Next thing you'll be worried about a chicken-and-cow uprising!*

FOX: (Finally getting the point) As long as we're together.

(They embrace.

(CUT TO sunset over the mountains to the west. The garden shines bright under the full moon, the frost is on the pumpkin. The sun disappears and as its last rays tuck behind the horizon, and night comes on, waves of bright leaves rush past the camera, soundlessly illustrating the approach of winter.)

*       *       *

End of Scene Eleven

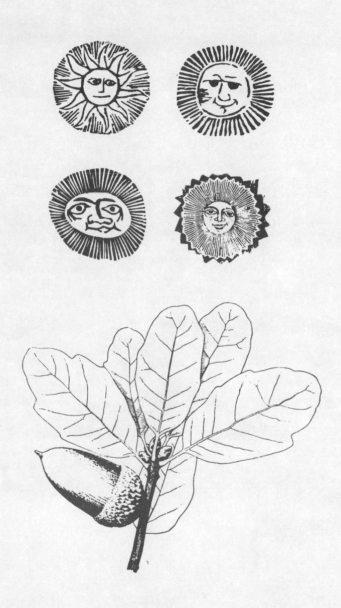

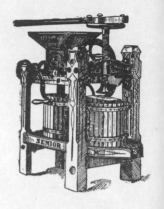

SCENE TWELVE

(Fall has reached its peak. The open barn door
reveals a hayloft fairly sagging with bales. The
sun is in Scorpio, and throws the most other-
worldly golden light on everything. The fields
are almost purple in color as a result of this
light, though I couldn't explain why. In the barnyard stands a proud solitary cider-press, the
old-fashioned kind which screws a wooden plate
down into a vat of bright red apples by means of
leverage applied by turning a long horizontal
pole on top. Two people, Jacob and Abraham, stand
on either end and walk about in a circle, pressing
apples into fine amber cider, which gushes forth
from a spout beneath the press into buckets. From
time to time, they drink it from a wooden dipper.

(In another corner of the land, in the background,
several people are cutting and stacking cord
wood. Even further into the background, Bessie is
grazing on the hillside, her cowbell gently tin-
kling, the sound of it carried far on the wind.
Abraham and Jacob stop pressing for a rest and sit
down on tree stumps.

ABRAHAM: O God, I just don't know anymore.

JACOB: *Know what?*

ABE: Everything. Why we're here. How we survive just to live, and go on with it, how things here can be so . . . har - monious . . . guiltless . . . I'm afraid again.

JACOB: *(His face reveals he's worried, but he tries to appear casual.) Aw forget it, it'll go away—*

ABRAHAM: Where?

JACOB: *California, maybe.*

> (CUT TO Pacific redwood wilds, the landscape has changed but the boys have not moved. It happens in a flash. Now the stumps are redwood, and it's summer again, everything's green.)

ABRAHAM: I dreamed of death, like it was coming over me, somebody's gonna die, maybe all of us, I've been listening to The Fox too much.

JACOB: *(Smiling, he understands) Well it's been clear we were all going to die since the beginning! They never did find the Fountain of Youth!*

ABRAHAM: (Seemingly oblivious to the good humor)

And . . . I don't know . . . something about love, I
need Ruth for sure . . . but suddenly I need a man to
love too. Do you understand?

JACOB: *It's not hard.*

ABRAHAM: Then you must know about how I also need to be
absolutely alone. God! If I could only learn to leave well-
enough alone! I mean nothing's wrong, the harvest was
good, but I got the crazy blues for moving around, maybe
even back to the city.

JACOB: *Boy! You got Karmic Kongestion, the city's behind us,
Abe, we can't really go there anymore.*

(CUT TO lunch counter in Washington, D.C., our two
heroes still seated and conversing, but now with
elbows resting on the counter and sipping coffee.
They are surrounded by black people of all ages
and appearance, all of whom ignore them
completely.)

ABRAHAM: Well we could take our *bodies* there with a lot of
work.

JACOB: *But our souls couldn't pick up on the jazzy music
again, we lost the tune, the city's all coo-coo
incomprehensible rubbish to us—*

ABRAHAM: Anyway there's a civil war going on in the city and I can't figure out—from *this* distance—who to root for.

JACOB: *Root for potatoes in Ireland and forget the civil war, we can't do anything to stop it. We can't even rule our own lives, it all just comes down from heaven.*

ABRAHAM: From the king.

(CUT TO an open convertible Morris Minor zooming through the prairie, Jacob driving, camera as before trained on their faces.)

ABRAHAM: Hey! I forgot I had this (reaching into his coat as he pulls out the Trust in the Lord dashboard placard the Negro-lady gave him in Scene Two.)

JACOB: *Where'd you get it?*

(FLASHBACK: Door of 1956 Buick slamming shut, sound of all-night news station on car's radio.)

ABRAHAM: (Smiling softly) A friend.

JACOB: *Lemme see—*

(Abraham starts to hand it over but drops it to the floor of the car. He bends down to recover it and comes up again back on the stump in the barnyard.)

ABRAHAM: O no, it's busted.

> (Jacob takes it, holds it up to the dying day-
> light. Where before it said TRUST IN THE LORD, it
> now says US IN HE O. The other letters broke off.)

JACOB: *"Us in He O." O!*

> (He allows his arm to drop into his lap, still
> holding the plaque.)

ABRAHAM: And we go under with the falling leaves. O god
sir, it's all so grandiose! I used to think I knew all about
everything, I was loud and precocious. And now I know
all about nothing, and I just want to be nothing.

JACOB: *If you mean dying, I doubt that it's really the end.*

ABRAHAM: Well at least it's not *words* all the time.

JACOB: *Heaven's silent, that's for sure.*

> (CUT TO Abraham and Jacob on horseback, silently
> thundering through a brilliant October after-
> noon, through a mountain pass, and into a valley
> dotted with teepees, crude A-frame houses, and
> geodesic domes made of plastic. Sign on a tree
> says "Mandrake Plains." In the center of the en-
> campment are perhaps 100 very young, very

strange-looking adolescents, and in their center
a youth with straight blond hair to the middle of
his back is ministering to a lovely girl who
kneels before him, his hand on her head. This vi-
sion lasts less than a minute, while Abraham and
Jacob water their horses in a nearby stream, and
go completely unnoticed. The girl rises, cured,
dazzled by the blond youth, unable to stop looking
into his eyes, and he leads her by the arm into a
large shanty and closes the door behind them.

(CUT TO Abraham and Jacob on the stumps again, but
now it is night and they have a healthy campfire
going between them.)

JACOB: (He sits now cross-legged, as in full lotus position,
head rocking back and forth almost violently.) No! I
refuse! I refuse!

ABRAHAM: (Has a dull glare in his eyes, seems hypnotized)
Refuse what?

JACOB: I refuse to have feelings that destroy me. Man, it's too
perfect. I destroy myself every time. I'm my own worst
enemy.

ABRAHAM: That's devil talk. The devil in you.

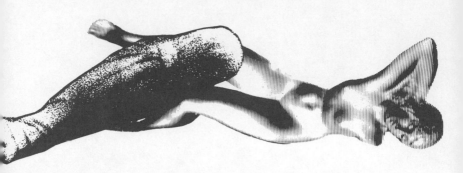

JACOB: *I don't know. I can't be responsible.*

ABRAHAM: Ah, we're all responsible. I don't know what the hell use *I* am around here for that matter—like I think I better split cause I got nothing to do here, nobody'd miss me . . .

JACOB: *Devil in you.*

ABRAHAM: The devil in me is just the guy that's always telling me *I can't make it,* I'm not strong enough, I haven't got it anymore. That's how I feel now. Like I just don't know how much longer I can go on. With nothing to do and nowhere to go.

JACOB: *O there's plenty to do. You just want to feel loved—by me and Ruth and Lisa. And you want to make love— that's what you want to do! Maybe you need a lover.*

ABRAHAM: You mean marriage? No, I tried that already. Marriage doesn't work.

JACOB: *Well it doesn't seem to. But I must confess I'm thinking I'd like to be married again for a while.*

ABRAHAM: You'd dig it for a while . . .

JACOB: *Well it would have to be a new kind of marriage you* know . . . I mean I don't want to possess anyone, I know it's impossible . . .

ABRAHAM: I don't know . . . You're setting yourself up for a fall. Setting yourself up for a fall. But I think it's just like the man said: "To have and to hold." So have! So hold! It didn't work before and it won't work this time or the next time, but that's no reason not to do it.

JACOB: Well, I guess you're right. It's always the same, it always falls through eventually, but we all go back to it again and again.

ABRAHAM: I didn't say we *all* did. You said that.

JACOB: You don't think you'll ever be married again? Ha, you'll meet somebody.

ABRAHAM: No. Not me. (Calm and convinced.)

(Ruth appears behind them. She too seems vaguely under a spell.)

RUTH: *The time I almost had twins. Everybody thought they were Samson's babies, but actually they were David's. The weekend I went down to New York, remember? That's where I got the babies. The abortionist had a white undershirt on, no shirt, and he was all sweaty and hairy.*

What hospital is this? *A troll for a midwife. My tiny, tiny bastards. Scooped out like cysts. I was going to marry David, he still sends me passionate letters. I threw away my bumbles. Who will bring my bumbles back to me? I loved Samson too, I found him in San Francisco, he was our angel, O we had so much pain together by the end there— nightly truce between venom and boredom—we curled together innocent as a pair of socks in the fresh laundry. Now my hands are like strangers. I'm getting a winter skin. Winter is long. To ail and sleep is a lifetime calling. After all these years, great love, I am finally consumptive.*

(Ruth reminds us of Isadora Duncan, so graceful and with the characteristic long scarf.)

\* \* \*

ABRAHAM: (Spastic and hysterical) Go way mean old devil! Go way! Go way!

JACOB: *(His arms around Abe's shoulder) Devil ain't got you yet brother, just a little while longer now and he'll be gone. Don't give in now, devil's a sure loser now you know that. Sure loser for you. Hold on there!*

ABRAHAM: Where's my gal? Where's my number one top banana?

(Ruth appears behind Abraham, and steps out of his shadow, pressing her open hand to his forehead.)

*RUTH: I'm right here now.*

(As she stops to the side, a full moon appears in the sky, a moon her shoulder had sheltered from our view. It's cloudy too, and the clouds race past that moon, heading for the eastern horizon . . . All three clutch and hug in a tight circle.

(CUT TO the loft in Chez Poulet, Ruth's cabin. Abraham, Ruth and Jacob are all in the bed covered to their waists by an old khaki Army surplus blanket. Ruth sleeps soundly between the two men, on her stomach with her head turned toward Abraham. Jacob sleeps on his side, facing Ruth, on the right side of the bed. Abraham is lying on the left side of the bed on his back, eyes wide open. He turns to regard Ruth and Jacob, it's clear. He's tired. He turns on his side and stretches his right arm to enwrap them both in single embrace, his elbow and arm across Ruth's back, and his hand in Jacob's hair.)

ABRAHAM: (Softly) O my dear friends.

(The moonlight plays on their bodies through the broken window. A cock crows. Abraham buries his face in Ruth's neck and hair and falls asleep.)

\*      \*      \*

End of Scene Twelve

## SCENE THIRTEEN

(As summer is earth, fall is air. Whatever it is
that brings out the devil in Abraham is traveling
on through an atmosphere charged with excitement.
As the colors explode and the thermometer collapses, the pace of work accelerates. Now the
barnyard is full of racing bodies chasing each
day's sundown as well as the eventual arrival of
winter, when outdoors work will be close to
impossible.

(Outside the mill at Spirit Lake, the day before
Hallowe'en. The Fox, Abraham, the vastly pregnant
Moonbeam and Mrs. Lawrence are nailing thick pine
shingles, cut by hand from foot-long logs with a
drawknife, to the exterior of a shack, which faces
on the lake. Standing nearby, hammerless, is a
nervous young man needing a shave, who paces back
and forth wildly gesticulating as he talks. He
talks incessantly, even when it is clear no one is
paying attention. This is Crane.)

MRS. LAWRENCE: (Mouth full of wide-ended
shingling nails) Nice of you kids to help me out

here, it ain't gettin no warmer outside! Wish I had some pretty curtains for that window.

*MOONBEAM: O I'll make you some calico ones right after I have the baby!*

MRS. LAWRENCE: From all appearances, that'll be soon. Now honey you're gonna have plenty to do once you have your baby, I'm not too old to make 'em myself, y'know. The curtains, that is. How ya feelin'? (Puts her hand on Moonbeam's belly.) Why you gonna pop open any minute now! (Throws her head back in laughter) O, I'll stand by you honey!

*MOONBEAM: Well . . . I'll let you know . . . it'll be Hallowe'en tonight. Is that a good time to have a baby? It's kinda spooky.*

MRS. LAWRENCE: Anytime's a good time for it, sweetheart, and don't you forget it! (Turns back to the shingling operation, grinning broadly, then notices Crane standing by.) And *you* boy, Crane! You got a broken arm or somethin'? Don't let this pregnant lady go hammerin' nails while you stand around in neutral!

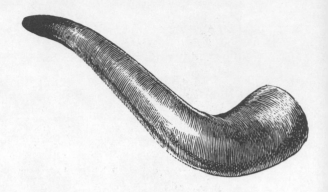

(He's been waiting.)

CRANE: Well now wait a minute, it's not like there's any finite and mutually-established amount of work to do, which if I lag on my part will necessarily be absorbed by Moonbeam (pointing to her) heavy with child. To the contrary, this shack isn't even of itself a necessity to the Spirit Lake community, although it's certainly *convenient* and pleasant for *you* at least (Mrs. L) to have the additional privacy it affords. But *my* name's not on a certain number of these shingles and if the mere fact that I'm not working with them convinces you that I'm somehow *shirking* my *duty,* then I'd say you're imposing some morality on these shingles which simply isn't inherent in them. It's like my stepmother used to make me put sheet-rock insulation in the roof of our house in New Jersey on the hottest days of July every year, and I had to wear thick, heavy clothing, including . . . INCLUDING . . . gloves and a hat, and I wasn't allowed to take a bath afterwards, and I'd get strapped and forced to lie in my bed with the windows all shaded up in the middle of the afternoon—without moving—all day long—and

not one day but every day and every night for a solid month. If I dared to even *suggest* that the work was too much for me.

Pardon me if I disturb your elysian psychedelic universe with these *grim* reminders of another world—but I've done enough work for a lifetime. The world there, the universe, is not small. It is large enough to include groups of men who, heavily dressed in metallic protective garb, and using mechanical hooks for arms, walk about in special laboratories owned by the government and the banks, carrying *paste of anthrax*—so deadly that the entire population of smaller countries can be wiped out merely by spraying it in specific areas, wherein the people contract one of several horrible diseases, all highly contagious. Forgive me, but those men are out there and *shit man* . . .

O I know you just want to do your simple bucolic chores, you're at least trying to *construct* something out of whatever's left—whereas I've become a *parasite* in any community—I can only succumb, quavering, to the darkness—you'll probably ask me to leave so you can protect this

live person from freezing in the winter instead of worrying the doom: you'd certainly have every right to . . .

The worst part of it is I think I'm about to become a *father* and that simply cannot *be,* though it seems to. I read in some psychology magazine that 83 per cent of battered children turn into *battering parents*—O God . . .

MRS. LAWRENCE: There ain't nothing to being a parent, it just happens to you.

CRANE: Well it's too difficult for me. I used to think there were maybe 35,000 people in the world and if you lived long enough you'd get to know all of them. You could live on some purple Scottish moor in a modest stone cottage with flowers in front, and listen to the distant train go by once every night. There wouldn't be many people on the train—it's only the train to Campbeltown. But it's not like that at all, and for a *baby* . . .

(All have stopped hammering now to listen to the monologue.)

ABRAHAM: (To The Fox) My God! Where did Crane come from, all of a sudden?

FOX: (To Abraham) He arrived here this morning, I sent a message to New York asking him to come, we're going to need all the people on our side that we can get when we finally come up against the Mandrake Plains—

ABRAHAM: From New York this morning! Well no wonder he's so far-gone. He'll be better after he's been out of New York longer.

CRANE: And *so:* for that reason and a thousand other incidents in my life as a battered child in this cocksucking nation, I've long ago decided to do: as LITTLE . . . actual . . . WORK . . . as I can possibly escape with, 'cause I've *paid my dues.* And I'm awfully glad *I'm* not having a baby!

FOX: I'm going there tonight.

ABRAHAM: Going where?

FOX: New York.

ABRAHAM: Why? How?

FOX: Crane left my car for me in a valley near here, I know how to get there. Why don't you come with me?

ABRAHAM: Why don't *you* stay home?

FOX: O don't be silly. I've got important business to take care of, we've got 250 half-crazed religious fanatics on our hands.

(Abraham looks at his hands, palms up. They are empty. He holds them up to The Fox in look-ma-no-religious-fanatics fashion.)

FOX: Besides, you could go to the movies.

ABRAHAM: I don't want to go to the movies, I want to enjoy this movie.

FOX: (His ace card) Well we've always gone together in the past. You won't let me go off all *alone,* will you?

ABRAHAM: (Holding his head in his palms) O God no.

FOX: No what?

ABRAHAM: No I won't let you go off alone.

FOX: I *knew* you'd be sensible finally! We can leave around sundown and find something to eat on the highway . . .

ABRAHAM: But I won't let you go to New York either—

FOX: (Heavy sigh) Someday you'll understand better, there's just some things you got to do. Forget I ever mentioned it.

ABRAHAM: Only if you'll promise me you won't go to New York.

FOX: (Long pause, then cheerfully) I promise.

\*       \*       \*

**End of Scene Thirteen**

SCENE FOURTEEN

(A large cabin-like room filled with all the people in this story except Moonbeam, Wonderboy,
Mrs. Lawrence and The Fox. Also present a dozen or
so newcomers, mostly young but one has a full head
of silver hair and a Vandyke beard.

(SILENT is playing a rich black concertina and
everyone is singing in exquisite harmony, "Amazing Grace." Silent smiles, rocking back and forth
in his chair. The chorus is straight from the
heart.

AMAZING GRACE

[words by John Newton, 1779]

Amazing Grace, how sweet the sound
That saved a wretch like me!
I once was lost but now I'm found
Was blind but now I see.

'Twas grace that taught my heart to fear
And grace my fears relieved;
How precious did that grace appear
The hour I first believed.

Through many dangers, toils and snares
I have already come;
'Tis grace that brought me safe thus far
And grace will lead me home.

(Camera pans all the faces singing, glowing by
candlelight and kerosene-lamp light in the room.
Outside it is darkest night. The song lasts perhaps three minutes.

(Camera flashes from this scene to Moonbeam's
bed, where the singing is still clearly audible
but muffled by the wall. The impression is that
her bedroom is next door to the congregation. She
is having her baby. Wonderboy and Mrs. Lawrence
are assisting. It is a boy. Its cries mingle with
the music. Moonbeam and Wonderboy are radiant.

(Camera flashes back and forth between the singing group and the birth of Noah. The singing grows
louder and more passionate: "Was blind but now I
see."

(Camera suddenly flashes onto outdoor scene. The
moon is still full, and casts a pale glow on the
trees. It is a forest scene, far from the house,
but we continue to hear the song.

(Slowly, as our eyes become adjusted to the moonlight, the shape of an automobile becomes apparent. It is some kind of sports car, the fast hyper-
sensitive variety. Camera moves in on it slowly,
eventually revealing a rubber hose connected from
the exhaust pipe leading into the vent window on
the driver's side. Through the glass, we can see
the body of The Fox, head tilted back, eyes open,
skin dark and tight, dead. Beside him on the passenger seat, an open newspaper.

(Flashback to Silent pumping the concertina,
grinning.

(Flash to the baby in Moonbeam's arms, bawling.)

\*       \*       \*

End of Scene Fourteen

SCENE FIFTEEN

(As fall is air, winter is fire. This is the dead
of winter; at no time does the west wind cease to
howl, nor the house to tremble. Snow is lashing
the roof.

(IMAGE: Total darkness on the screen. The
darkness nonetheless has shadows and the camera
seems to be moving through it, searching for
light. This goes on for perhaps ten seconds, to
the sound of the blizzard outside. Finally in the
middle of the screen a door seems to clank open in
the darkness, and we see the inside of a fiery pit;
just the view into a top-loading Ashley Automatic
wood-burning stove; the intense light inside is
perfectly framed by the door, and then a hand is
seen throwing chunks of hardwood in. The sounds of
that. Then the camera slowly moves to the face of
this person, illumined by the firelight. It is
Silent again, smiling into the flames.

(He slams the door shut, and the screen is plunged
into darkness again. You can hear him walk to another part of the room. Perhaps he bends down to pet

a dog, and you can hear the sound of the dog panting. Then silence for a moment, then the sound of
a striking wooden match. He lights a large kerosene lantern with a red glass bowl and some black
deposit on the glass chimney. In the soft light we
can see that five people are sitting in a sort of
circle not far from the Ashley stove. Each one of
them seems to radiate a feeling of great internal
peace and warmth, the group as a whole radiates it
too, at the same time it is clear they are atten-
tive to the storm going on outside.

(Abraham is leaning back with his hands clasped
behind his head. His eyebrows are raised, his eyes
closed, his head rocking slightly forward and
back. Next to him Ruth is balancing a small steaming teapot on the arm of her chair, which is large
and heavily-stuffed and falling apart, tilting to
the left, where Mad John and Marie are sharing a
love-seat.

(Silent sits among them, and as he sits down, Ruth
pours the hot brew into a large cup. She passes
this to Abraham, who drinks and passes it on, and
so until it's been around a few times, and is
empty. The pot and the cup are put back on the

table and everybody leans back and perhaps closes his eyes to wait for the effect, what may be, of the drink. Very slowly it becomes apparent that something IS going to happen, and the audience is meant to lean back in the same way.

(Jacob appears on the fringe of the group, smiles, picks up a twelve-string guitar and begins to strum a beautiful melody, what seems to be the introduction of a song the group will sing. But it is very long, and soon seems to be the counterpoint of the storm outside. This musical introduction continues and builds, but the people just look at Jacob intently instead of singing. After a while he stops. Then there is only the now-increasing sound of the wind and snow carrying on Jacob's song.

(Suddenly the sound increases enormously, surely the sound of wind and snow we'd hear if we went outside.

(The louder sound precedes the visual change of scene by about two seconds.

(NEXT IMAGE: In dim moonlight and snowlight outside in the storm, Silent comes through the door

and closes it. The snow makes his face unrecogniz-
able; he's bundled in a great Army-surplus parka.
This image is sudden and different, as when you
suddenly realize you've been sitting somewhere
stoned for a long time.

(Still a showman at heart, Silent looks around and
dances a little jig in the snow. The blurriness of
snow-vision makes him seem to move very very
slowly and almost to float above the ground. He
waves his arm and three dogs materialize out of
the storm, Mamoushka so white and two of her puppies. They all set out; they know the trail but it
is indistinguishable to us. Shapes of trees can be
made out behind them.

(Now they are all standing at a crossroads; the
image is one that emphasizes the closeness of
space in a storm at night. The wind sweeps across
them and the sound is ear-shattering; the dogs
don't go far off; one of the puppies is terrified,
and sits by Silent's leg, leaning against it and
shivering, whining. Silent sees a small light in
an abandoned house about 10 feet distant; as he
walks to it, the light is like a glowing sphere of
snow.

(He peers in the window of the shack. Inside, around a fireplace, two old bums, hobos, with long grey beards, two vagabonds of the forest are cooking up some coffee and rice in No. 10 cans, wrapped in heavy coats they are breaking up what appears to be rare early furniture to feed their fire. Next to them a very young woman is breast-feeding a baby. The old man furthest from the window is singing, but we cannot hear the words. The other man realizes they're being watched, and slowly turns to face Silent; when their eyes meet, the old man smiles beatifically; the smile is a long time forming and spreading over his face. Then this image disappears into snow.

(Silent is again standing at the crossroads, the puppies beside him. Then he and all the dogs play, leaping falling and rolling in the snow. This action slows down then, and the sound of the storm slackens a great deal while they lie still a second.

(This new sound is the sound of the storm as it was heard inside the house, and within two seconds the image changes back to the room inside. Silent is in, takes off his coat and hat, knocking off the snow. He warms himself by the stove and then sits and quietly rocks in the rocking chair. There seems to be no one else around. Then the light picks up Ruth, who's been lying on an elevated couch behind Silent's head. She props herself up on an elbow, looks around and asks him: )

RUTH: *Did you have a good walk?*

(This is the only line spoken in this scene. Silent looks round him, sees Ruth, nods his head. )

\*       \*       \*

End of Scene Fifteen

## SCENE SIXTEEN

(IMAGE: Brilliant winter dawn. Pink flush on the
eastern horizon. The entire village as seen from
afar by Abraham in Scene Three, but the hills and
trees are entirely white under a blanket of fresh
snow from last night's storm. Only an occasional
never-say-die weed or sapling pokes out from under this unscarred pure carpet.)

NARRATOR'S VOICE: Winter came on slow and gradual like
always, but still there was definitely one day, one morning,
that was the first day of winter; that's the morning when
you wake up and realize everything on the whole earth is
inaccessible to you without a lot of struggle until the
spring. And we never knew when spring would arrive. It
seemed like forever.

With The Fox gone, we were lonely. Somehow it was *our*
fault that he didn't live to crack the frost, so we didn't
wonder about his *reasons* for doing it or anything, we knew
all along how it would end. But it was so hard to stay
warm then, even with so many of us left still kicking and
sudden war with the Mandrake Plains and eventual
insanity in the whole village. The colder and snowier it
got, the crazier we became, it's called "cabin fever"

sometimes. And the endless pastoral image of ourselves posing against the land locked in ice like a poem wasn't enough, somehow, to overcome the strange spirits which blew in on the wind.

We buried The Fox on a Monday, by Wednesday the earth above was frozen solid as slate. Mamoushka got her winter coat. The food ran out.

(The SOUND of a tremendous dynamite explosion. It seems to be coming from over the mountain, that is from behind the village, some distant point beyond our view.

(IMAGE: Doors opening from the houses in our panorama, people rushing out to fill the yard, obviously confused and agitated about the source of the great noise.

(SOUND: A second explosion, then a third. Several of the figures in the yard race around the house and head up over the mountain, disappearing behind the forest line.)

NARRATOR'S VOICE: The only trouble was there was nothing to do. Or else we *thought* there was nothing to do, I guess it's all the same. We managed to fill the vacuum.

It was an era of great religious rebirth, when I was young.

A thousand small gurus and avatars, many of 'em pretty good at it, pretty smart y'know, were going around blessing everybody and gathering followers, it was like we all expected the end of the world to be just around the outhouse. But even the One Cosmic Mind had to find its component parts and before long one little master couldn't coexist with another, heretics were born, and religious war replaced political conflict among the youthful hip initiated. Just like a million million times before, other places other times, but the basic story's the same: power.

We were just trying to survive and have fun, but the Mandrake folks believed in neither so they couldn't tolerate our vibrations.

(Abraham, Jacob and Marie come into view, sledding on a homemade toboggan into the plateau community of Mandrake Plains. They arrive near the first house and disembark, walking together toward the door while pulling their sled behind them.)

MARIE: *Ab-rahm?*

ABRAHAM: Yeah?

MARIE: *You remember what I have tell you the ozzer night about these ones?*

ABRAHAM: Yeah, you said the Mandrakes was a black magic cult and Gregory was a warlock and they'd poison us. And do you remember what I answered?

MARIE: *(Ignoring his question) Would you believe me if I told you I was under hypnosis that night?*

(Abraham catches a very far-away glint in Marie's eyes and decides to calm down the rising tone of her questions.)

ABRAHAM: Aw come on, who hypnotized you? (Laughs.)

MARIE: *(Angry, intense) You don't believe me!*

(Jacob whips out a pocket harmonica and groans a few low notes, forming a little melody.)

JACOB: (Crooning) *My my my, don't tell lies!*

MARIE: *It was Ruth!*

ABRAHAM: Now why would Ruth want to hypnotize you?

MARIE: *Because I speak the truth now I throw away my sheet. (She flings her arm forward to illustrating "throwing-away" her shit.) And now I see you all MAD and you bring me here to make me mad too!*

ABRAHAM: Are you mad?

MARIE: *(Far-away) No. Thanks God I am still not crazy. But YOU, man, you very crazy—you French man, ah I HATE you French man. Like my fazzer.*

ABRAHAM: Your father was French, I'm not.

MARIE: *Ya. Thass right. You EXTRA-TERRESTRIAL.*

ABRAHAM: (Trying to turn the moment to a joke) Extra-T! I'm an Extra-T! And when I'm asleep at night I'm actually wrestling with Martians and receiving my orders from foreign planets. My astral body *takes off* while my poor earthly form momently dies. C'mon, what kind of conversation is this?

JACOB: *(It's a routine from the Psychic Vaudeville Show.) Let's have a conversation!*

ABRAHAM: Have a chicken!

JACOB: *Have an egg!*

ABRAHAM: That's rich!

JACOB: *Can I call you a cab?*

ABRAHAM: (Glint in his eye) Where's the other half?

> (Marie is not amused by their banter. She steps between them, hands on her hips.)

MARIE: *My fazzer was crazy like you. He laughed so much he died. When . . . when he make love to my mozzer, it was violent and strong like you not man enough to be. (Addressed to both of them) American man! How I despise American man!*

ABRAHAM: (Interrupting, but no longer laughing; staring at the ground) A minute ago we were French.

MARIE: *(Ignores him) I had a brozzer too, but my fazzer kill him when he is born, because he didn't want no more children. He kill him in my bed while I was little girl—O and he take him out and get rid of him.*

*I remember now what I have forgotten. It was just at the end of the war, I was very little, things was very confused then and nobody find out. The army of liberation was in the streets of Chatelet, we hear all the people singing and yelling through the window—it was an afternoon in Paris, my mozzer was with me in bed, she said "Don't cry, CHER TRESOR, de Gaulle has ended the war now, the bad time is over now, good time begin now."*

(CUT TO Paris. A small room, obviously French, a bottle of wine half-drunk and portion of a loaf of bread and some cheese are sitting on a small

table. Marie is asleep on her side in a great dou-
ble-bed backed against several bookshelves;
beside her, in the middle of the bed, Ruth is reading As I Lay Dying by William Faulkner. On the bed,
open, a copy of the magazine Planete. Abraham,
naked, is at the foot of the bed, crouched on his
haunches and writing on the wall of the room with a
Magic Marker. There are many things written on the
wall, "honi soit qui mal y pense" and lines in
French by Ramakrishna and R. D. Laing's saying "If
I could turn you on, if I could drive you out of
your wretched mind, if I could tell you I would let
you know." Under the line "Marie, je t'aime,"
signed Nadine, Abraham is writing "Moi Aussi,
Abraham."

(During this brief flash we hear snatches from the
Santana song, "Black Magic Woman." "She's a black
magic woman/Cast your spell on me baby/Turn your
back on me baby."

(Back to Mandrake Plains. This turn stops both
Abraham and Jacob cold in their snowtracks. We get
the feeling it's something about the karma of the
particular land they are standing on which brings
out this sudden hostility in Marie, who minutes

earlier was happily sledding through the woods.
All three stand stock still for a moment. The land
is curved in a way that suggests it is warped: the
cornfield itself bulges up in the middle like a
poorly made wooden floor, and sits under a tall
and unusually sharp peak now just black and white
except for occasional patches of evergreens. All
of the other slopes in the area are soft and
rounded.

(The main cabin of Mandrake Plains is like a Han-
sel-and-Gretel cottage of white pine planks
nailed to thin 2-by-4 joists, with a sharply-
peaked snow-covered roof. It stands on stilts 12
inches off the ground, and seems impossibly frail
considering the harsh weather. There are only a
few windows, and these very small. On the outside
wall of the house are painted the "RULES OF MAND-
RAKE ROOTS" in crude block letters. The rules include "No drugs," "No fornication," "No minors
overnight," no no no except for the last rule
which reads simply "Gather Infinite Understanding." The door swings open and a pretty young
girl in ankle-length dress appears.)

*GIRL: Hello! Can I help you?*

JACOB: O! Yeah, we're from Spirit Lake and . . . er . . . we heard all these incredible explosions this morning about dawn and were wondering if you knew what it was.

GIRL: (Cheerfully) O yes, that's Gregory and the dynamite crew. They're blowing up the mountain between our place and yours!

(Abraham is amazed. He turns pale as a ghost. Marie is fairly buzzing with curiosity, she's smiling again.)

ABRAHAM: Blowing up the mountain! What?

GIRL: (Still pleasant, almost like a hippie-stewardess cross) Won't you come in?

(Inside it is very dark, but we can see there are clearly at least 30 or 40 people in one room. Most of them are just sitting on pillows and old carpets along the walls, some are burning incense and pretty candles, several including the blondheaded Gregory are standing in the center of the room around an ugly great stove made of a converted oil-drum. There's a tremendous buzz, a crowd noise, as the newcomers enter and Gregory turns from what he was doing lecturing a young girl, his arms around her shoulders to greet the visitors.)

**GREGORY:** (Extending no hand) You've come at last.

ABRAHAM: (Nervous and shy) Yeah. (Looks around) Big group you got here.

**GREGORY:** There are 150 others working in the woods now. We need space from them to eat and sleep. Are you ready?

ABRAHAM: (Doesn't get it) Hunh?

**GREGORY:** Are you ready to throw open your doors to the Lord?

    (Tom and Richard from Scene Eleven appear from behind Gregory, as out of the darkness, and stand one on either side of him like bodyguards. All three are somber.)

ABRAHAM: Well I'm sure we wish you the best, man, but . . . ah . . . we've got quite a few people ourselves, and some new babies and stuff . . . I mean we haven't even got extra beds really.

*JACOB: Space, space, they all want space.*

**GREGORY:** That's not good enough, and you know it.

    (Abraham is fearful and confused and knows he's in the wrong place. He turns to Jacob and Marie.)

ABRAHAM: Let's go.

(He and Jacob turn to the door, but Marie remains gazing on Gregory with a fixed stare. Gregory returns her intense gaze. They are, together, locked in a trance.

(Abraham touches Marie's arm as if to signal let's go. She turns to him briefly, blankly, then back to Gregory.

(Abraham and Jacob softly approach the door, almost on tiptoe. All the noise in the room has come to an absolute silence. Everyone stares at the departing pair except Gregory and Marie, who continue to look at each other. They leave her with him and exit.

(Outside, Abraham grabs the rope on the toboggan and begins to tug it uphill again, tucking his six-foot long blue scarf into a dark blue pea-jacket and pulling a knit cap over his head with his free hand. Jacob's been wearing a pullover waist-length leather poncho all this time, reaches into his back pocket for a floppy old hat. Together, they walk away.)

JACOB: *Did you hear what that cat Tom said? "Smoking of dope must be ruthlessly eliminated."*

(Abraham's response is to reach in his pocket and produce a blue cigarette, which they stop to light and draw deeply on as they walk.)

ABRAHAM: Did you see the way she looked into his eyes?

(A tremendous explosion behind them, but they don't turn around to see it. We can see trees, earth, snow flying through the air.)

ABRAHAM: (Pensive) It was like a *church* or something; you know what I mean, it wasn't like home.

JACOB: *Religion's a funny thing.*

ABRAHAM: So who's laughing? (This is a mock Jewish-mother intonation. They both laugh.)

JACOB: *(Wrapping his arm around Abe's shoulders) Don't worry about Marie, she'll be back.*

ABRAHAM: (Stops walking, looks Jacob straight in the eye) I doubt it.

(SOUND: A thirty-second reprise of James Taylor: "Rock-a-bye Sweet Baby James.")

\*     \*     \*

End of Scene Sixteen

**SCENE SEVENTEEN**

(Abraham and an old Negro man sitting on big rocks
alongside a swiftly moving stream, which tumbles
over the rocks, forming rapids, and gleams in the
winter sunshine like diamonds. Mamoushka has both
front paws in the cold clear water, and is gamely
trying to catch a fish in her mouth, without suc-
cess however.)

OLD MAN: *To catch a fish around here you gots to get up early
in the mornin', cause that's when the fish is sleepin' you see,
cause he so lazy, haw haw—*

(He extracts a very good-sized trout from his bag
and slaps it down between them with a laugh.)

ABRAHAM: To catch a fish sometimes you have to be a bird.

OLD MAN: *Well, now I don't know: don't take no chances,
though, you goin' far and if you fly high ye might always
fall down.*

ABRAHAM: I'll take the risk.

(The fish between them abruptly moves. Its
breathing apparatus on the underbelly quavers and
its large rear fin flaps.)

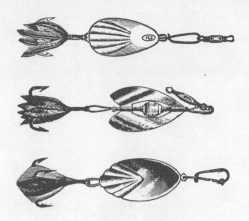

ABRAHAM: (Staring at it) Jesus! Did you see that? You know, I wonder if it would come back to life if we put it back in the water.

(A pause while both of them examine the still fish. Then it shudders once again, and Abraham empathetically shudders with it, but the old man remains calm.)

OLD MAN: *Now you kin try and bring it back to life if you wants to—YOU the only one can do that—don't try to goad me on to do it, cause I ain't that crazy, h'yes, and I reckon to EAT this here fish for my dinner up to the farm.*

(A pause, then Abraham grabs the fish as if to toss it back in the water. But something stops him cold and he freezes in position with it. Fear and sadness on his features. Finally:)

ABRAHAM: No. The fish must die. It stands between us.

(He begins to cry, loud sobbing tears. The old black man puts his arm around him. Abraham drops the fish, which moves no more, to the ground.)

OLD MAN: *And the bird is born, eh?*

\*     \*     \*

**End of Scene Seventeen**

## SCENE EIGHTEEN

(IMAGE: The Cafe Depresso. The round table has been cleared of everything but a gigantic round candle, unlit, which sits dead-center on it. Abraham and Ruth sit opposite each other on stools, each playing solitaire. They lay out their cards one-two-three-four-five-six-seven in standard solitaire fashion, in exact counter-position on either side of the table. Outside a big window behind Ruth we can see it is snowing. We can also see one apple tree which has been pruned so that its branches reach out as if to heaven in everywhichway twisting confusion, but stop short where the cuts have been made. On each of these cuts rests a perfect circle of snow, perhaps six inches in diameter and two inches deep.

(Abraham and Ruth are talking to each other energetically but there is no sound at all on the track. It's a silent movie.

(Uncle Louie enters through the double-door dressed in a checkered woodsman's shirt and enormous black wool trousers held up by red suspenders. Mad John enters carrying a banjo, which he

is tuning up with intense devotion. Mrs. Lawrence
bursts through carrying a big casserole dish full
of rice-and-vegetables, steaming. A middle-aged
man with greying beard and long hair passes
through in a Continental-gentleman outfit topped
by a red beret. Several young women with babies in
arms. Wonderboy carrying a 250-pound anvil on his
shoulders.

(All these people are talking and laughing. All is
confusion.

(Beneath them, subtitles are flashing in standard
block-letter subtitle fashion. The first reads:
TALKIE-TALKIE BLAH BLAH BLAH. A pause. The second
reads: AH HAH HAH BOO HOO HOO. Pause. The third
reads: DANCE TILL THE COOKIES ARE DONE. Pause. The
fourth reads: YOU'LL NEVER GET PAST THE TREES.
Pause. The fifth reads: STRIVING TO UNDERSTAND.
Pause. The sixth reads: IT'S ALL THE SAME!

(Each subtitle rests on the screen at least three
full seconds, and each may be synchronized with
some particular action in the room. By the sixth
subtitle, IT'S ALL THE SAME!, the room has filled
to bursting with people. Abraham flails both arms

in the air as the sixth subtitle comes on, and all laugh uproariously.

(The seventh and final subtitle reads: YOU NEVER CAN TELL.)

*       *       *

End of Scene Eighteen

## SCENE NINETEEN

(IMAGE: The Green Room. This room is like a library or study; bookshelves made of thick hemlock planks, cut from trees at the Spirit Lake mill, line two of the four walls. The other two walls are bright green, hence the name Green Room. There are two windows but it's night outside and they are black. A cloth sampler stretched into a wooden frame hangs left of center on one green wall. It reads NEARER MY GOD TO THEE. On the other wall, a large heavy portrait, perhaps a daguerreotype, of an old white-bearded man in formal 19th-century dress. Against this wall is a long print-pattern sofa, the 50-year old overstuffed kind with fat arms on either end. On the floor, a thin carpet. In the corner, an old cast-iron potbelly stove and a neat stack of split logs. This stove has little isinglass windows which are glowing red.

(Abraham is sitting to the extreme right of the sofa, directly under a bright kerosene lamp, which is placed against an upright oval mirror for maximum light. Mirror and lamp stand on a homemade

three-legged endtable. Abraham is reading a big
old dusty book.

(We take in this quiet scene for only a split-
second when we hear the SOUND of a door slamming
hard. Abraham looks up from his book with some
alarm. Less than a second later, Marie steams in
at a run, throws her arms around him, knocking the
book to the carpet. We see her back only now, her
body completely obscures Abraham. After hugging
him tightly for one or two seconds, she releases
him and he jumps to his feet. Then they sit at
opposite ends of the sofa, both with their feet
curled up under their bums, and begin to talk.

(Marie is covered with snow from head to foot, but
she does not seem conscious of it and she doesn't
bother to remove her outer clothing. After a
minute or two, she begins to drip all over the sofa
as the snow on her coat, hat and boots starts to
melt.)

MARIE: *I thought something had happened to you.*

ABRAHAM: (Still stunned by her entrance) I'm . . . I'm fine.

MARIE: *Ya. Thass good. (She pronounces ''that's'' as
''thass.'')*

(Pause. They stare at each other.)

ABRAHAM: How are you?

MARIE: *Fine. Sure.*

(Pause.)

MARIE: *I thought you were dead.*

ABRAHAM: Not that I know of. Here I am!

MARIE: *Ya. I see you now. Before, I was blind. Now I see you fucking game. I don't play you fucking game anytime more.*

(Her words are not angry, but drained of emotion altogether. She continues to look at him with a fixed stare. He cannot stand it and shifts his gaze to the floor, the lamp, the window, but always returning to look at her again.)

ABRAHAM: (Obviously searching for something to say) Did you enjoy your visit with Gregory?

MARIE: *(Nodding her head up and down slowly) Ya. I understand many things now. I thought you was walking the same road with me to truth and EXTASE. But I see now you just after POWER (she spits this word out) just*

*like the ozzers, you no different than the ozzers, you just want POWER, you and Jacob togezzer. You just want to set up your little world here and destroy every one who try to walk the good road, you just don't hear or see any ozzer one but yourself.*

ABRAHAM: I'm not going to try . . . try to defend myself.

*MARIE (Once again nodding) Ya. I talk to Jacob tonight too, at Spirit Lake, and I tell him what I tell you.*

ABRAHAM: That you love him?

*MARIE: (Far-away) That I love two men who love only each ozzer.*

> (FLASHBACK: The loft in Chez Poulet, three half-exposed sleeping figures, exactly the same tableau as at the end of Scene Twelve, except the sharpest eye will notice that the woman in the middle is no longer Ruth, but Marie.
>
> (IMAGE: Marie's face fills the screen. Her eyes are wide open, green. Her face is wide, with high cheekbones, strawberry blonde hair, and a few freckles. She's still talking.)

*MARIE: Ya. Gregory was right. You live for nozzing here but you food and house and clothes, you have no faith to*

*live by here, just you sheet, which I throw away. You*
*steal from Gregory his chance to be higher, you pollute*
*his infinite understanding. I rather be low among the*
*higher people, real people, than highest queen among you*
*low people.*

(Her voice has become throaty and low and tired.
There is still no anger in it, just like all this
is a simple recitation. Camera comes in even
closer until Marie's nose and eyes and eyebrows
fill the entire screen. Her eyes are a little
bloodshot, and we can now see Abraham, sitting
curled up and shivering, reflected in the corners
of her eyes. Behind him, the isinglass windows of
the stove appear like tiny red pinpoints.


(Marie's eyes fill the screen, but Abraham is now
talking.)

ABRAHAM: Power is not my game—not anymore. It was once.
I used to ride fast in the city and talk all the time and
stage confrontations—O, I was ruthless and sinister then. I
climbed to power on the heads of my enemies, and my
whole program was to destroy the powers that were—
governments, churches, schools—cause I intended, without
admitting it, to replace them, and be a government of my

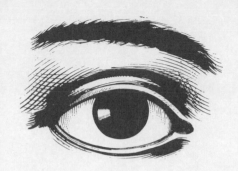

own—not only to myself, but to everybody. I was a real bastard, you don't know.

I was poor then, cause there was always something I wanted and couldn't get—poor and mean and petty. Then I got my three wishes.

My first wish was to be rich. I wanted to have everything I wanted, that is I wanted to *want nothing*. That one was too easy. Pretty soon I was richer than a king, I wasn't hungry or tired or cold anymore and when I thought about it, I couldn't imagine what possible physical thing I needed. After you get what you want, you don't *want* it anymore. And the less you want, the more you *have*. Like Ruth said, "Lower your aspirations!" So I wanted nothing.

I went back to the genie for my second wish and wished for love of men and women and all the critters that scarf on our ground. I wished to be able to make love and be loved by my brothers and sisters on the planet. That's where you came in, you remember. You taught me a kind of womanlove that I didn't know before. You saved me. You know that, don't you? It was in Scotland that time with Ruth and Shining Youth—that blond boy. We saw the snake crushed in the road, and a cock crowed three times at us in a green field in Switzerland.

So you know about my third and last wish too. This is a dream we're living in, our lives have become a *dream,* that's our Provincial Reality now, and I wished to *wake up.* Lord send me *awakening.* Silent. Age of Silence is what I want, I'm tired of dream farms and movies now. Like that night we saw the lightning, you remember. It was real dark and real quiet and this weird never-before-seen kind of lightning was lighting up the black sky into perfect daylight, with blue skies and clouds and sun, it was like a sign, a taste of awakening, and we sat out in the barnyard watching it all night.

And what's come between us is something I don't understand except when the demon takes hold of me. What keeps us from being lovers anymore. I don't like it, what's come between us, but I know we're strong enough now to survive it—cause we got the three wishes. See?

O, and it won't end, Marie, you know that too. *They're not going to let us die!* Modern science will immortalize us and we'll be geriatric teenagers playing "Lucy in the Sky With Diamonds" one more time.

(Long pause. Then Marie speaks.)

MARIE: *Just today I realize who was leading you black magic cult. Ruth. I don't know how I was blind so long, so*

*long. She is like the serpent, who wrap you in her arms and cut off you blood. And to Jaa-kob too. And thanks God almost to me, thanks God but I get away just in time.*

(She closes her eyes. The IMAGE shifts to Spirit Lake, the great central mill, its wheel merrily turning. Long icicles hanging from the roof. There's a full moon shining brightly on the snow. Camera rests on this moon for ten seconds. Thick white clouds race past it. When the clouds are gone by, the moon shines with a glowing ring around it. When the clouds cover it, it is dimmed to a small white shape with no ring. The SOUND, however, is still the conversation between Marie and Abraham.)

ABRAHAM'S VOICE: It's all . . . it's all in your mind.

*MARIE'S VOICE: Ya. And my mind is free now, and I set the animals free and now I set YOU free.*

ABRAHAM: The animals? (For the first time, he sounds terrified.)

*MARIE: (Dreamily) The dogs, pigs, chickens, LA VACHE, Jacob's horses . . .*

(IMAGE: The mill at Spirit Lake. Lights burning brightly inside the main rooms, but we still cannot see in.)

ABRAHAM'S VOICE: The horses don't belong to Jacob. The mare is ours and the stallion . . . (a hoarse whisper): the stallion!

MARIE'S VOICE: *Ya. Iss funny you make these animals objects of the big love. So I show you how easy it is to lose . . .*

ABRAHAM'S VOICE: O Jesus!

(IMAGE: The mill at Spirit Lake. A wide door on the lowest level of the building swings open, flooding the snow-covered yard with light. A chestnut bay mare trots out, bows her head, walks slowly into the night, then halts, as if unwilling to go further. Behind her by a few seconds is a grey stallion with flowing mane, who bolts from the open door like a shot and races off in the snow. The mare takes off, following him. These are the same horses ridden by Abraham and Jacob in Scene Twelve.

(Marie's voice is crying.)

\*　　　\*　　　\*

End of Scene Nineteen

## SCENE TWENTY

(IMAGE: The mill at Spirit Lake. First we see the
outside as in the last scene, then a quick cut to
inside, where a tremendous bash is underway. Mad
John is playing an electric guitar powered by a
small generator in a corner of the room. Backing
him up, a group of perhaps ten musicians: Uncle
Louie on a gigantic set of conga drums, Silent on
concertina, a thin young man with bright eyes working a shiny set of trap drums with the insignia
"IWW" on them, several people on backup guitars,
Ruth on wooden recorder, many others banging tam-
bourines, percussion sticks, etc., or just clapping and stomping their feet. John is the prin-
cipal vocalist. He sings a musical version of Rob-
ert Frost's poem, "Fire and Ice."

Some say the world will end in fire,
Some say in ice.
From what I know of passion and desire,
I hold with those who favor fire.
But if it had to perish twice,
I think I know enough of hate

To say that ice is also great
And would suffice.

(In the center of the room is a large open fire
which vents into a copper chimney, stovepipe
variety, leading to the peak of the roof This is,
of course, the focal warmth of the room. Everyone
seems ecstatically happy, the whole scene is
pulsating.

(The song, "Fire and Ice," is the only sound in
this scene.

(There's also a Fire and Ice ballet going on outside. It is in perfect harmony with the music.
Camera cuts quickly to the grey stallion and
chestnut mare racing across the snowfields and
over the mountain. There is a certain madness to
their gait, parallel to the madness in the music
and also indicative that Marie, or somebody, had
frightened them. They are running neither to nor
from any particular place. The stallion leads the
way at first while the mare, a standard bred,
maintains a disciplined trot. But the snow is too
deep and eventually she comes broadside him and
they run together. In the moonlight, we can see
them approaching the Mandrake Plains encampment.

There are great holes in the earth everywhere, the two horses dance around them.

(CUT TO Abraham running as hard as he can, accompanied by Mamoushka and her puppies, along the road from the village to Spirit Lake. Mamoushka is fast and keeps a few paces ahead of him, but the puppies have to struggle to avoid falling further behind. All four move at a breathless, hard-breathing, gallumphing gallop, similar to the horses.

(CUT BACK TO the happy scene at the mill. The tempo speeds up for the second chorus and the volume increases. Everyone's dancing.

(The series of images is repeated one more time, as with the song, faster and more frenzied. First the horses, then Abraham and the dogs, then the musical ensemble.

(The song ends with a tremendous explosion. The stallion tramples a cache of dynamite left on the ground by the blasting crew. Both horses are consumed in the explosion.

(Abraham arrives at the mill, flinging the door open and, panting, collapses on the floor.

(The band finishes on a frenetic note, then the music stops abruptly as several people rush forward to attend to Abraham.)

*       *       *

End of Scene Twenty

SCENE TWENTY-ONE

(IMAGE: The living room at the mill, Spirit Lake.
Dawn is creeping up outside, all the windows getting progressively lighter. Some folks are sleeping on couches and mats here and there on elevated
platforms.

(Uncle Louie is in a corner, smoking a cigarette
and softly beating his big drums. He is chanting
over and over, but almost in a whisper: "I am not
afraid, I am not afraid."

(Abraham and Ruth are together on one of the mats,
but still wide awake. She is sitting upright in
full-lotus position, he is resting his head in her
lap.

(Jacob is having an intense, but quiet, conversation with a curly-headed young man who stands
only five foot three. Junior. This fellow illus-
trates his remarks with graceful, sweeping ges-
tures, like a knight/messenger to the court.
Jacob mostly listens, occasionally striking a
chord on his guitar in counterpoint to Uncle
Louie's drumming. Whereas all was frenzy a minute

earlier, there is now a strange calm over the
room. Junior starts his story.)

JUNIOR: All I know is what I can see and feel. You
know me. Just the facts.

I was coming up from the city in my car, and I
couldn't get further than the lower pasture, cause I
ran it into a snowbank down there—so I had to hike
up through Mandrake Plains and I figured to stop
there for a cup of tea or something. But by the time
I was on the edge of Mandrake Plains something
stopped me cold.

I heard voices but I couldn't make out what they
were saying. It was dark. I heard a tremendous
explosion. I heard what sounded like a Russian
army advancing on the Ukraine. Clomping boots and
everything, and singing like the Volga Boat Song.

Then the voodoo came over me. It was a tall
bearded man talking very fast in Spanish. I was in
his power, I was terrified and the only way I could
make him go away was to say "Water," but *I
couldn't speak.* I was trying to say "Water," but for
a long time nothing came out and the voodoo kept
rapping in Spanish getting more hysterical and more
threatening all the time.

They were all around me. The Russian songs, the thumping boots, a few babies crying, the voodoo yelling in Spanish "Buen fuerte! Buen fuerte!"

Then the forest opened before me. The sun rose and I was at the Mandrake Plains house. The cookshack. But the people were all gone and the house was all blown to shit, pieces of things here and there. After that, I saw the horses.

JACOB: *I'm not surprised, that 16-year-old kid who was in charge of the dynamiting, he was so spaced out, he didn't know what he was doing, playing with dynamite . . .*

JUNIOR: All I know is what I can see and feel. The horses are there, at least you can see parts of them; the cookshack is all blown out and the west wall is down completely, so it's full of snow and ice; and otherwise, not a soul.

JACOB: *But where did they go? Did you look around to see if anybody was hurt maybe?*

JUNIOR: I looked everywhere. The only thing I can guess is that they left together sometime before sundown yesterday. Um . . . there was a full moon in Gemini, as you probably know. All the animals

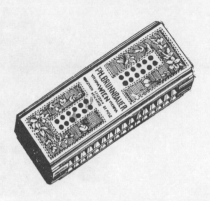

stuck around the barn at home except for the horses, and, I don't know, maybe the cold drove 'em out. The people, that is.

**UNCLE LOUIE:** *(Interrupting his chant) Seasonal saviors?*

**JUNIOR:** Anyway, there's nothing we can do now except wait for daylight. Leave it up to me. We'll work it out.

*JACOB: Do you think they'll be back?*

**UNCLE LOUIE:** *(Again) Ha! Do you think they were ever there in the first place?*

ABRAHAM: (From across the room) They'll be back.

(Everyone is silent. The light in the room grows stronger and stronger. Silent begins a mournful air on his harmonica. One of the dogs, Lightning, seems to react to that particular musical pitch, and he sings along. Gradually, the old narrator's voice returns and the people, one by one, drift out of the room. Those who were asleep wake up, those who were not simply walk away. Finally the camera is resting on an empty room, and every chair and platform seems bereft of its intended spirit.)

NARRATOR'S VOICE: They never came back, and neither did Marie. We later heard stories about Gregory being in trouble with the law, but that stuff came in second-hand and we couldn't be sure. The room I'd left Marie in was all in a shambles when we got back to it, but we didn't care about that too much. There was a note from her too. It said: "It's all the same here, but wherever I go, it's never the same. I'll remember you."

There was something about the mountain that resisted anyone's trying to gain power over it. I saw lots of people try and fail. You had to live there on its terms, and only the mountain made the rules. Everybody who tried to organize us, or presumed we were there as a political party, church, or movement, or tried to create a reason for our being there just went down choked with meetings and misunderstandings and argument. All you could do in that place was live in it.

The stallion was wild when we got there. It was one of a herd that grazed around Spirit Lake before we built the mill. He never belonged to us. Only Jacob could ride him and he'd had some bad tosses on 'im, although at times the stallion could be just as calm as you'd like. Anyway, the rest of the herd disappeared once the community was established, so we didn't think it'd be fair to let him go.

Only Jacob had any chance of breaking him, and only Marie could have set him free.

*     *     *

**End of Scene Twenty-One**

SCENE TWENTY-TWO

(IMAGE: Dinner in the Depresso. The table is set
for ten with earthen mugs and wooden bowls and
spoons. Yale, the cleancut collegeboy from Scene
Five, has made a thick soup in an enormous black
Wok. A Wok is a Chinese saucepan, it looks like a
miniature flying saucer, shallow and round. Yale
ladles out heaping bowlfuls for everybody and a
pitcher of Bessie-milk is passed about, as well as
steaming bread and several plates with great yellow lumps of butter. Everyone oohs and ahs.)

*WONDERBOY: Let's have fish-cakes tomorrow night!*

**RUTH: No, silly, we'll have Rhoda tomorrow night.**

ABRAHAM: Is it time already?

YALE: Yup. Pork-chops, ham, bacon, yummy!

(Abraham and Silent regard each other with know-
ing looks. They are the vegetarians of the bunch.)

MRS. LAWRENCE: (Just like a mother, slapping
Yale's hand as he reaches in to begin his soup)
Haven't you forgotten something, sonny boy?

YALE: (Regaining his dignity) Ah yes! Will you do the honors tonight, Ruth?

> (Ruth is a little taken aback, but quickly shifts in her seat and crosses her hands in her lap.
>
> (All bow their heads.)

RUTH: *God help us refugees in winter dress, skating home on thin ice from the Apocalypse.*

WONDERBOY: *Can we have fish-cakes the night after, then?*

\*       \*       \*

End of Scene Twenty-Two

L. JOHNSON & CO

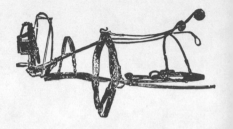

## SCENE TWENTY-THREE

(SOUND: Chickens cackling, clucking, occasionally a rooster hoots. It is early morning, we hear
early-morning sounds, we're in the barn. There is
hay everywhere, huge wood beams overhead, a sec-
tion with gunnysacks full of grain, feed for the
animals, a few farm machines, a plow, harrow, all
these old and rusted, yet obviously in use. They
might be driven by a modern tractor or a team of
oxen, we aren't really sure, for the good sights
and sounds of a barn, and this barn in particular,
transcend time and space.

(Ruth is milking Bessie. The door to Bessie's
stall is open and we can see it's still winter.
Bessie exhales wafting streams of frost-air from
her nostrils. Ruth is wearing a long dress to her
ankles, covered by a worn pair of overhauls rolled
up at the cuffs to halfway up her calf, and black
boots. The milk falls into the pail plink! plink!
plink!

(Abraham is standing against one wooden wall of
the milking shed, he watches Ruth doing the
milking, he munches on a roll freshly baked. He's

wearing a faded woolen cap, thick sweater, overalls.)

*RUTH: (Still milking, looks up at Abe) Today's the day, isn't it?*

ABE: Yeah, I guess it is. (Pauses.) Let me know if you get tired, I'll finish her up if you want.

*RUTH: Don't be silly, I do this every day. (She continues, the white liquid streaming into the bucket.) They need a little more grain, though, it's over there.*

ABE: Sure. (He picks up two metal bowls and walks over to where the gunnysacks are, fills the bowls, then sets one bowl in front of each cow, pats their noses.) I'm sure glad we're not going to eat you, Bessie.

*RUTH: You don't have to eat any, then, but I think you're being ridiculous.*

ABRAHAM: Who knows. I suppose if you're going to eat meat and all, you should love it and raise it and kill it yourself; that way, at least, you're aware of the sacrifice involved.

*RUTH: They used to have* **Human** *sacrifices.*

ABRAHAM: Human sacrifice. They *still* got human sacrifice. That's it: if I eat Rhoda, how do I object to somebody's eating *me* one of these days?

**RUTH:** *(Laughing) Well that's bound to happen anyway. So you don't eat Rhoda, so you eat just carrots and potatoes and cheese and eggs and stuff like that—you're still going to get eaten up yourself in the end! The big mother is gonna swallow you up whole. The earth—the new moon—the king. Anyway what makes you so sure that carrots don't have feelings too?*

(Abraham spreads his arms and spins around in a circle until he is giddy.)

ABRAHAM: Big mother eat me up! Yum yum heart and lungs of me for dessert. Yum yum! (Stops spinning.) Do you suppose we'll be *digested* too?

**RUTH:** *Sure! We'll turn into planet poop!*

ABRAHAM: (Roaring with laughter) Planet poop! I can't wait! (Suddenly serious, he looks directly at Ruth with open eyes, through Bessie's tits. Camera sees his eyes on opposite sides of the front two udders.) They will let us die then, you think? We won't be geriatric teenagers after all, you think?

(Ruth shrugs her shoulders, finishes off Bessie, walks around the cow, handing the heavy milk pail to Abraham, who has to use both hands to grasp it.

She smiles discreetly but she is tired of the
conversation.)

RUTH: *There's nothing to dying. It's getting born that's tough.*

(She exits, he remains.

(AS WE CUT TO overall shot of the front of the
farmhouse, still early morning, there is a grey
tone to the film, almost as if we'd switched from
color to black-and-white. Nothing moves for a few
minutes, it is almost an oil painting we're looking at. All of a sudden the front door opens and we
can make out four or five young men, their faces
grim like they're at a funeral or going to one. Abe
is the last one out. Close-up of his face, worried, better-said apprehensive: the boys walk in
single file over to the barn, then around the
side, down a few steps and into the lower shed. We
follow them. The first one in line has a shotgun in
his hand, he holds a box of shells in the other. He
is taller, though approximately the same age as
the others, middle twenties. We watch them enter a
fenced-in area, it's the hog-pen. There is a long
thin trough with water in it, a thin layer of ice-
crust is forming over the water, snow is everywhere, though not very thick. The other boys carry

a roll of brown wrapping paper (otherwise known as
butcher's paper), a long rope, several meat-cut-
ting knives, their blades large and dark. Two pigs
walk around slowly, it is clear from their faces
that they know what is about to happen.

(WE CUT TO a bright green field, almost electric
in contrast to the black-white-grey scenes we've
just been immersed in, this field green and in the
middle of the summer is like a flashback or a
barely-remembered dream. Two pigs munching on the
grass, the middle of summer, hot sun out; the
scene lasts not longer than 1½ minutes.

(WE CUT BACK TO the hog-pen, the five or six boys
standing around, they've encircled one of the
pigs. But the pig isn't about to run away or anything, she knows what is to take place, she (for
generations) has been reading the same script.
One of the fellows throws the rope around her
neck, then he stands a few feet away from her, but
the rope hangs limp like a garden hose. The tall
boy with the shotgun now stands a few feet from
Rhoda, the pig, and he raises the rifle so that it
looks her square in the face. We get a close-up of
the pig's face, eyes small and evil though under

the circumstances our sympathies might tend to lie with her, camera moves around the circle of boys standing outside, their faces cold, grey, the trees bending in the wind, the camera comes to rest on Abe's face:

ABRAHAM: (In a voice as cold as ice, the man fighting hard to hold back the boy inside whose stomach is turning and whose hands are like cold sponges) Do it already (barely audible).

(We hear a loud gunshot, though the camera is still on Abraham's face, mouth clinched tight like a clam's. The film is very stark, perhaps actually in black-and-white.

(SOUND: As soon as the gunshot is heard we hear the Incredible String Band singing "Big Ted":

Big Ted was a pig, he was a good ol' pig,
He ate all the garbage and he never wore a wig,
But he's gone, he's gone, he's gone
Like snow on the water

Let me be a milk cow, next time round,
Giving sweet milk to all the people of the town,

(The following scene is played out to the sound of the song: the boys hang the pig upside-down and

open a hole in its throat, the blood runs out into
a wide tin bucket. Then they take the scraper-
combs and begin to scrape the bristle off its
hide. They are round the animal like children
reaching for a streamer on a Maypole, but their
faces are still tense. We watch Abraham, he does
his work, but he's getting sick. The song-music in
the background ceases for a moment, and we hear
him say:)

ABE: Oh, I just remembered I told Silent I'd feed his dogs this
morning, I'll see you all later. (He blurts this last out, like
he can't stay another moment, then turns and runs out the
hog shed.)

He's gone, he's gone, he's gone
Like snow on the water.

\* \* \*

End of Scene Twenty-Three

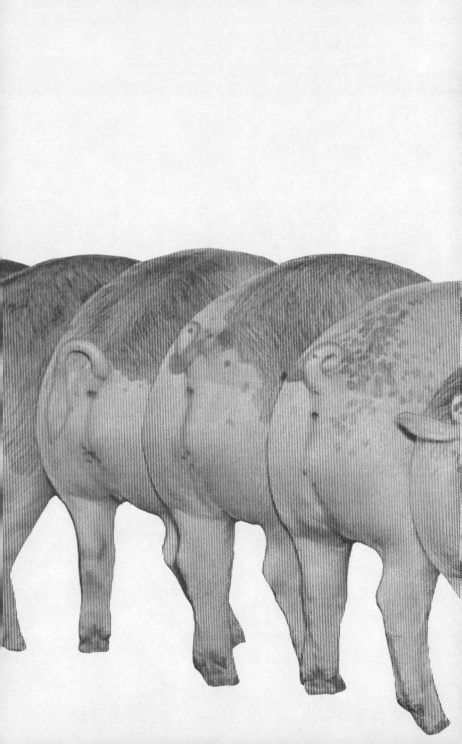

SCENE TWENTY-FOUR

(IMAGE: The forest deep in snow. It is very late in
the winter now, and the snow is very deep. There's
still a fierce wind. One way we have of measuring
the lateness of the season is that the snow
reaches up to only a foot or so short of a group of
signs nailed to a tree. One sign reads FROM THE
FARM with an arrow to the left. Another says
SLEAZY PINES with an arrow straight up in the air.
Other signs are partially buried under the snow.

(Abraham and Big Marty are putting up dull grey
buckets on the maple trees. They stop at each maple, drill a hole in it with a hand-drill, then
rush to plug a wooden spigot in each and hang a
bucket on the spigot. Mamoushka, incongruously,
has been hitched to a big wooden sled loaded up
with buckets and spigots, and she pulls their sup-
ply from tree to tree. At one point, they come upon
a rushing tumultuous brook. The water is roaring
through and they are forced to leap over it with a
running jump. Abraham almost falls in, teeters
for a moment, then rights himself. They discon-
nect Mamoushka from the sled and yank it over with

a rope, losing several buckets in the process,
while Mamoushka deftly scales the stream. They
laugh.

(The snow-crust is soft now, and they fall through
it repeatedly, sinking in snow to their knees and
struggling out of it again.

(As the day wears on and the sun gets stronger,
both of them are too hot in their heavy pea-
jackets and scarves, and both strip them off and
work in their shirt-sleeves.)

ABRAHAM: Hey Martee! How come the sap is flowing now
when it didn't used to?

BIG MARTY: *Haw! I don't know. Cause it's warm in the
afternoons and cold at night, I think.*

ABRAHAM: When do we get to boil it down to maple syrup?

BIG MARTY: *Aw, we can do that tonight on the kitchen
stove, onaccounta there ain't enough good wood left
to have a separate fire for it.*

ABRAHAM: Yeah, I . . .

(He stops dead in his tracks, and without saying a
word more, starts off to the right, up a hill,

running as best he can in the deep snow. About 20
feet up there's a graveyard surrounded by a
fieldstone fence. It's the same graveyard Abe
discovered on his way to the village, but now the
headstones are deep in snow and only the tops of
them are showing. He runs over to the grave of
Rebecca Chapman and notices, with astonishment,
that the headstone is now lying flat out on the
snow, its message facing up to the sky:

Rebecca Chapman
1762–1781

Two weeks I bore affliction sore
Physicians' skill was vain.
But in the end death came as friend
to ease me of my pain.
Death is a debt, from all 'tis due
Which I have paid and so must you.

The grave is open. It's been dug up, not very
recently because the hole is lined with fresh
snow, but nonetheless it's clear Rebecca is no
longer there. He clears the stone with his gloved
hand and reads it again. The grave alongside it is
also empty, as before.

(Camera zooms in on Abraham's face. In his eyes is reflected water, the rushing brook catching the sunlight and bouncing it back and forth. Just water. We hear Big Marty's voice as from afar: "Abe! Abe! Where the hell are you?!" We hear Mamoushka barking. Still we see only his face and the water. We hear the sounds of moving water, the steady uninterrupted woosh and roar.

(Still looking straight ahead, Abraham says:)

ABE: Let's go home now.

*       *       *

End of Scene Twenty-Four

SCENE TWENTY-FIVE

(IMAGE: The mill at Spirit Lake in bright sunlight. The lake is thawed now and the water-wheel
turning fast and furious. The SOUND of water, moving water, is deafening now. The roof of the mill
is showing through bright blue, the road is black
and spongy mud, and the snow on the open fields is
broken here and there by patches of brown, gritty
grass.

(There's a tremendous commotion in the yard. Many
rugs are being hauled out of the house, spread on
the snow, and tromped soundly by eager dancing
feet. When the rugs are lifted from the ground,
the snow remains black with dust and soot and the
rugs are bright and colorful again.

(A crew of men is trying to move a cart drawn by two
oxen. The cart has sunk into the mud on the road to
over its wheels, and nothing will make it go.

(CUT TO the main village house and barn, where the
scene is much the same. Ruth is hanging clothes on
a circular clothesline behind the house. Abe
sneaks up behind her and grabs her around her
waist, begins to cart her off like Tarzan or

something in the direction of Chez Poulet. Both shriek and laugh over the sound of the water.)

RUTH: *Abe! Watch it, you'll hurt the bumble!*

ABRAHAM: The what?

RUTH: *The bumble.*

(Abraham is astonished, and stands back to devour Ruth with his eyes. She begins to cry, they meet in a long embrace, and plop to the ground under the clothesline in each others' arms.)

\*　　\*　　\*

End of Scene Twenty-Five

SCENE TWENTY-SIX

(IMAGE: The hillside overlooking the village, as
Abraham first saw it. The last of the snow is gone
now and, although the trees are still bare of
leaves, they have just budded. The grass and trees
are, thus, green, but the green is as delicate as
first-run maple syrup. It's the moment after winter, the moment before summer.

(Abraham and Ruth, who now has a small pot-belly
where The Bumble lives, are lying in the fresh
grass taking in the scene, which is littered with
humanity. Perhaps 200 people are there, everyone
who's appeared in the movie at any time, many
babies, packs of dogs running around, some old
people, a tremendous number of musicians playing
light and delicate airs on violins, harps, recor-
ders, light instruments. No electric rock this,
but a Maypole merrie gathering.

(The entire ensemble is carrying a tall Maypole up
the hill. The pole is festooned with crepe-paper
streamers in bright pastel colors. Most of the
people are dressed in gaudy middle-ages minstrel
attire, very beautiful and finely-woven, but some

are naked. Every kind of reprehensible erotic
frolic is going on at once. There is no focus to
it, but music, gaiety, and near-hysteria fill the
air.

(Abraham has eyes only for Ruth and her bumble. He
lies down to catch a nap in the full afternoon sun,
resting his head in her aproned lap. She too lies
back and, shading her eyes with her arm, falls
asleep. They smile angelically.

(Bessie appears in the center of the barnyard with
a calf so young it can hardly stand.

(Camera rests on Abraham sleeping.

(Gradually the SOUND of the music changes from
light pastoral airs to calypso. Ai yai yai yai.
Someone is singing a love song about a mule in
Spanish.

(Ruth's apron under his head turns into a print
bedspread on a small comfortable twin bed.
Abraham wakes up, his eyes bursting open, he sits
bolt upright with fear and astonishment written
all over his face. He puts both palms down on the
bed and looks around: it is a small stateroom on a
ship, with modern furniture, radio, etc.

(He turns to the door of the room, light "blonde" varnished wood, and races through it, down a long corridor lined by similar doors leading to other staterooms, and onto a deck where middle-aged tourist types and a few long-haired down-and-outs are listening to a Jamaican steel band and dancing vaguely Latin steps.

(From the deck of the boat, which is just setting out to sea, he sees the city of Scene One over a calm harbor ocean. The sun is setting somewhere behind the city, a pink flush lights up the entire smoky sky over the buildings, and is reflected in the water.

(The South American rhythm grows stronger and the music louder as camera loses Abraham, gradually, into the holiday crowd aboard the ship. Our last glimpse is of a wide-eyed speechless Abraham, not frightened but surely innocent of his situation, on the path of another dream.)

\*       \*       \*

THE END

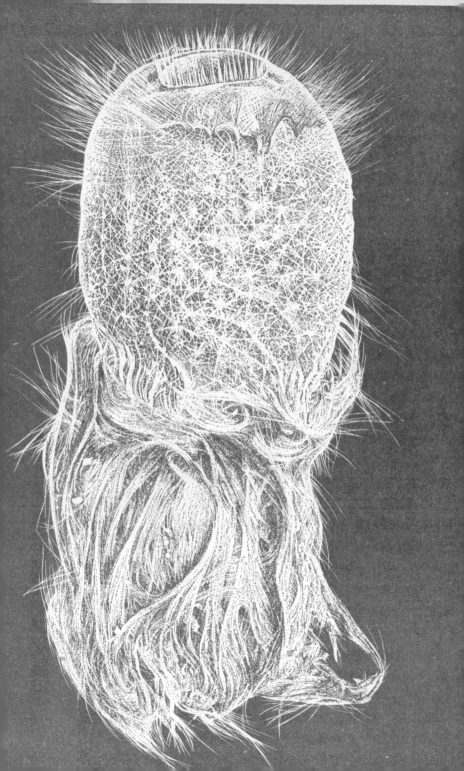

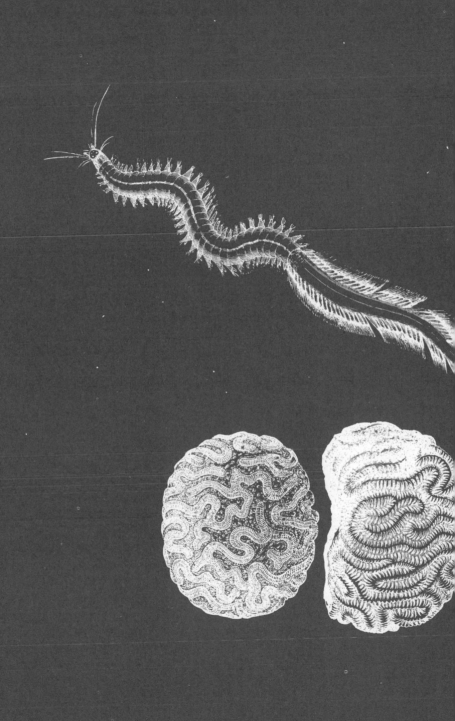

**EPITAPH**

THE NARRATOR: I left the village for only one reason, to die.

Somehow we always managed to survive as long as we stayed in that one place, guarded on all sides by the impregnable psychic mountains, by thick walls of hope and candor and new mornings. The rhythm of the planet itself rescued me time and again.

But paradise is only made to be lost, and when my number came up I had to go. Some stronger force than my will, call it destiny or Karma-earned fate, drew me irresistibly, with a magnetic attraction, into the arms of a strongman who killed me. How could I go on living after what I'd seen?

From the village I sailed to Costa Rica and steep green mountains in tropical sunlight and rain; there I lived with The Fox, reincarnated I'm pleased to say, and in the flesh; it was in the shadow of the Sierras del Muerte, or Mountains of Death. But it wasn't till months later, in still another dream, that I met my end: in New York City.

There, I married the devil and made myself game for his lust. He loved me and filled me with precious genius, he

plowed me and I bear fruit. I became him and tempted still others. I died and went to Hell.

I died and went to Heaven. My agony turned to ecstacy overnight, and perfect love came through; I couldn't believe my luck. The dark demon stabbing my groin shocked me into the light; I saw stars; and it was St. Michael himself with fluttering wings, I became Leda and godhead, I rose again.

All this transpired in a twilight era in the dying years of Earth, before we took to the heavens and luckily escaped the general mind-holocaust which brought that planet into its second millennium after Christ. All this vibrated between two moons, and both of the moons were me.

Between two moons, between Heaven and Hell, dark and light, between yin and yang, lies that imaginary dividing-line or ideal center called god, or the golden eternity, or nothing at all since words can only distract us from it. Between the halves of your body, at your sexual center, lies one of a thousand gates. Open it.

Between us, writer and reader, me and you, nothing but that same invisible line, which also binds us. You're dead too.

Vermont, Costa Rica,
Luna & Philadelphia
1970–1971